*B. Kainka and H.-J. Berndt*

# PC Interfaces under Windows

## *Measurement, Control and Regulation under Windows*

Elektor Electronics (Publishing)
Dorchester, England

**Elektor Electronics (Publishing)**
**P.O. Box 190**
**Tunbridge Wells**
**England TN5 7WY**

**British Library Cataloguing in Publication Data**

A catalogue record for this book is available from the British Library.

**ISBN 0-905705-65-3**

Cover design:   Ton Gulikers, Segment bv
Translation:    Geoffrey Home
Layout:         Kenneth Cox

Copyright © 2001 Elektor Electronics (Publishing).
First published in the United Kingdom 2001.

Printed by Wilco in Amersfoort, the Netherlands.

# Contents

**Foreword** . . . . . . . . . . . . . . . . . . . . . . . . . . . . . . . . . **6**

**1 Introduction** . . . . . . . . . . . . . . . . . . . . . . . . . . . . . . **7**
   1.1  PORT.DLL . . . . . . . . . . . . . . . . . . . . . . . . . . . . . 8
   1.2  Visual Basic 5 DLL calls . . . . . . . . . . . . . . . . . . . . 10
   1.3  Delphi DLL calls . . . . . . . . . . . . . . . . . . . . . . . . 16

**2 The Serial Interface** . . . . . . . . . . . . . . . . . . . . . . . . **21**
   2.1  Serial interface DLL functions . . . . . . . . . . . . . . . . . 23
   2.2  RS232 access in Visual Basic . . . . . . . . . . . . . . . . . 24
   2.3  RS232 access in Delphi . . . . . . . . . . . . . . . . . . . . 29
   2.4  Access using port commands . . . . . . . . . . . . . . . . . 34

**3 Direct Digital Outputs** . . . . . . . . . . . . . . . . . . . . . . . **41**
   3.1  Timer clock . . . . . . . . . . . . . . . . . . . . . . . . . . . 41
   3.2  Driving servos . . . . . . . . . . . . . . . . . . . . . . . . . 44
   3.3  Controlling stepping motors . . . . . . . . . . . . . . . . . . 52

**4 Direct Digital Inputs** . . . . . . . . . . . . . . . . . . . . . . . . **57**
   4.1  Computing transitory events . . . . . . . . . . . . . . . . . 57
   4.2  Simulating digital logic . . . . . . . . . . . . . . . . . . . . 60

**5 Simple Analogue / Digital Converters** . . . . . . . . . . . . . **63**
   5.1  Resistance measurement . . . . . . . . . . . . . . . . . . . 63
   5.2  Voltage measurement . . . . . . . . . . . . . . . . . . . . . 66
   5.3  Four-channel A/D converter . . . . . . . . . . . . . . . . . . 71
   5.4  Transistor measurements . . . . . . . . . . . . . . . . . . . 76

# Contents

**6 Frequency Measurements** . . . . . . . . . . . . . . . . . . . . . . . . . . . **81**

6.1 Software counter . . . . . . . . . . . . . . . . . . . . . . . . . . . . . . . . . . . 81
6.2 Measuring air temperature and humidity . . . . . . . . . . . . . . . . . . 85
6.3 Voltage / frequency converter . . . . . . . . . . . . . . . . . . . . . . . . . 90
6.4 Frequency plotter . . . . . . . . . . . . . . . . . . . . . . . . . . . . . . . . . . 95

**7 Synchronous Serial Data Transmission** . . . . . . . . . . . . . . . **99**

7.1 Serial output . . . . . . . . . . . . . . . . . . . . . . . . . . . . . . . . . . . . . 99
7.2 Serial input . . . . . . . . . . . . . . . . . . . . . . . . . . . . . . . . . . . . . 106
7.3 Serial A/D converter . . . . . . . . . . . . . . . . . . . . . . . . . . . . . . . 109

**8 Multi-purpose Interface** . . . . . . . . . . . . . . . . . . . . . . . . . . . . **113**

8.1 Hardware and its control . . . . . . . . . . . . . . . . . . . . . . . . . . . . 113
8.2 The Compact Universal program . . . . . . . . . . . . . . . . . . . . . . . 118
8.3 Automatic IC tester . . . . . . . . . . . . . . . . . . . . . . . . . . . . . . . . 122

**9 The Parallel Printer Port** . . . . . . . . . . . . . . . . . . . . . . . . . . . **129**

9.1 I/O lines . . . . . . . . . . . . . . . . . . . . . . . . . . . . . . . . . . . . . . . . 129
9.2 Bi-directional printer interfaces . . . . . . . . . . . . . . . . . . . . . . . . 133

**10 Parallel Data Outputs** . . . . . . . . . . . . . . . . . . . . . . . . . . . . . **137**

10.1 Function generator . . . . . . . . . . . . . . . . . . . . . . . . . . . . . . . . 137
10.2 Controlling simple machines . . . . . . . . . . . . . . . . . . . . . . . . . 140

**11 16-bit Port Expansion** . . . . . . . . . . . . . . . . . . . . . . . . . . . . . **145**

11.1 The 8243 port chip . . . . . . . . . . . . . . . . . . . . . . . . . . . . . . . 145
11.2 Expansion to 32 port lines . . . . . . . . . . . . . . . . . . . . . . . . . . 148
11.3 EPROM programmer . . . . . . . . . . . . . . . . . . . . . . . . . . . . . . . 153

**12 The I$^2$C Bus** . . . . . . . . . . . . . . . . . . . . . . . . . . . . . . . . . . . **161**

12.1 Data transmission and addressing . . . . . . . . . . . . . . . . . . . . . 161
12.2 Control via the parallel interface . . . . . . . . . . . . . . . . . . . . . . . 163
12.3 Serial interface connection . . . . . . . . . . . . . . . . . . . . . . . . . . 167
12.4 PCF8574  port expansion chip . . . . . . . . . . . . . . . . . . . . . . . . 170
12.5 PCF8591  A/D and D/A converter . . . . . . . . . . . . . . . . . . . . . . 177
12.6 Storage oscilloscope . . . . . . . . . . . . . . . . . . . . . . . . . . . . . . 180

# Contents

**13 The Joystick Port** . . . . . . . . . . . . . . . . . . . . . . . . . . . . . **189**

   13.1 Analogue & digital inputs . . . . . . . . . . . . . . . . . . . . . . . . . . 190
   13.2 Voltage measurement . . . . . . . . . . . . . . . . . . . . . . . . . . . 196
   13.3 Threshold monitoring . . . . . . . . . . . . . . . . . . . . . . . . . . . 199
   13.4 Switched output . . . . . . . . . . . . . . . . . . . . . . . . . . . . . . 202
   13.5 Digital counter . . . . . . . . . . . . . . . . . . . . . . . . . . . . . . . 205
   13.6 Joystick driver calls . . . . . . . . . . . . . . . . . . . . . . . . . . . . 208

**14 Sound Cards** . . . . . . . . . . . . . . . . . . . . . . . . . . . . . . . . . **213**

   14.1 Recording and playback . . . . . . . . . . . . . . . . . . . . . . . . . . 217
   14.2 An oscilloscope in Excel . . . . . . . . . . . . . . . . . . . . . . . . . . 218
   14.3 An oscilloscope in Delphi . . . . . . . . . . . . . . . . . . . . . . . . . 220
   14.4 Computed sound output . . . . . . . . . . . . . . . . . . . . . . . . . . 225
   14.5 Hearing tests using the sound card . . . . . . . . . . . . . . . . . . . . 228

**15 Video Capture Cards** . . . . . . . . . . . . . . . . . . . . . . . . . . . . **233**

   15.1 Picture display . . . . . . . . . . . . . . . . . . . . . . . . . . . . . . . 233
   15.2 Colour information . . . . . . . . . . . . . . . . . . . . . . . . . . . . . 242
   15.3 Measuring length with a video camera . . . . . . . . . . . . . . . . . . 243

**16 Asynchronous Serial Data Transmission** . . . . . . . . . . . . . . . **247**

   16.1 Reading data from a serial mouse . . . . . . . . . . . . . . . . . . . . . 248
   16.2 Digital control via RS232 . . . . . . . . . . . . . . . . . . . . . . . . . . 251
   16.3 ST62 microcontroller UART . . . . . . . . . . . . . . . . . . . . . . . . 256
   16.4 A serial bus . . . . . . . . . . . . . . . . . . . . . . . . . . . . . . . . . 267

**Appendix** . . . . . . . . . . . . . . . . . . . . . . . . . . . . . . . . . . . . . **283**

   References . . . . . . . . . . . . . . . . . . . . . . . . . . . . . . . . . . . 283
   Index . . . . . . . . . . . . . . . . . . . . . . . . . . . . . . . . . . . . . . 284
   PORT.DLL Reference . . . . . . . . . . . . . . . . . . . . . . . . . . . . . 287
      Port Commands . . . . . . . . . . . . . . . . . . . . . . . . . . . . . 287
      Serial Interface Routines . . . . . . . . . . . . . . . . . . . . . . . . 287
      Soundcard Routines . . . . . . . . . . . . . . . . . . . . . . . . . . 290
      Joystick Routines . . . . . . . . . . . . . . . . . . . . . . . . . . . . 292
      Timing Routines . . . . . . . . . . . . . . . . . . . . . . . . . . . . . 294
   CD-ROM Contents . . . . . . . . . . . . . . . . . . . . . . . . . . . . . . 296

# Foreword

Most of today's PC's are independent of the old DOS operating system at the user level, even though some underlying code has evolved from DOS routines. The widespread adoption of Windows has brought increases in user comfort. On the other hand, many hobbyists regret that numerous broad possibilities, which were not a problem under DOS, have now disappeared. A Windows program cannot exercise full control over the computer in the same way as a DOS program.

Under DOS, a large number of very simple applications were developed that provided direct access to the PC interfaces. LEDs and simple switches could be connected directly to the COM interface, for example, without any additional resources, and simple circuits could also be directly controlled. Under Windows, this simple approach appears to be blocked. However, we would not take the trouble of making this long introduction if there were no solutions available. The objective of this book is to demonstrate the possibilities of direct access to interfaces under Windows.

The aim of this book is, among other things, to encourage the use of readily available and cost-effective control circuitry. The text has been developed from an older DOS-only work, and beside the older applications there are some new project possibilities that arise under Windows. In general, only Windows 95/98 is used in this book. The preferred programming languages are Visual Basic and Delphi, which are the Windows successors to GW Basic and Q Basic, and Turbo Pascal. Many existing DOS programs can be relatively easily ported to the Windows environment.

We wish our readers every success.

Hans-Joachim Berndt and Burkhard Kainka

# 1

# Introduction

Every computer experiment in real-time process control or supervision, first requires a suitable connection to the outside world. A program must be able to record external information, to capture data and control external equipment. Data can be in either, binary (0/1), Boolean (.true. / .false.), or in analogue (continuously varying signal) format.

The gateway to the outside world has traditionally been through interfaces. Industrial standard PC's, i.e. IBM PC's and clones, are obliged to follow the format of established interfaces, such as.:

- Industrial interface cards installed in the computer, which have the highest throughput but are also the most expensive.
- Standard PC interfaces connecting the computer to external interface circuits. Usually for example, RS232 serial interfaces are used, which are relatively cheap to build.
- Independent single processor interfaces controlling complex tasks and having extensive data reduction capabilities, and without any raw data exchange with the PC. The application program must in this case, also comply with the system programming requirements and the user must also deal with the programming of these microcontroller systems.
- The presently available PC interfaces: the serial interface, the printer interface and often the joystick interface can be directly used as outside world connections. Thus in many cases there is no need to use additional hardware.

# 1 Introduction

The availability of directly connected interfaces is quite useful, particularly for simple experiments. For example, they can be used with the serial interface without any further amplification for directly driving LED's, and they have very interesting project possibilities. The printer interface provides a large number of high-speed direct connections.

Many limitations can be overcome with simple additional circuits. Voltage recording is possible with only a few extra components if somewhat more complex programming and slightly lower execution speed are acceptable. In addition, projects with many I/O lines are possible without any significant additional effort.

Generally, the methods introduced in this book use few additional components, but are complimented with somewhat more demanding programs, so the PC's CPU has to work a little harder. The reader needs to be experienced with a programming language and have some electronics knowledge. Most of the circuits are so simple they can be easily built on experimental boards. All projects in this book are described completely and are easy to experiment with. In addition they provide a basis for the reader's own developments. The more complex applications require some use of appropriate measuring instruments, i.e. the reader should for example have an oscilloscope.

The programming languages used in this book are those designed for the Windows 95/98 operating systems, i.e. Visual Basic 5, and Delphi 3 & 4. All program code can be found on the CD and in the book.

## 1.1 PORT.DLL

The specific problem under Windows is input from the PC interface, so a universal DLL has been devised, written in Delphi 3. A DLL (Dynamic Link Library, a Windows function library) is a set of routines which can be called from Visual Basic procedures and loaded and linked into a user application at run time. These can also be provided for other programming languages, and exclusively for this book a bespoke PORT.DLL has been developed, which can be found on the CD. Once the DLL is copied into the

Windows system directory it can be used by every program. Alternatively it can be consolidated into the program directory of an *.exe file. PORT.DLL has the following functions:

- Opens the interface
- Controls serial data transmission
- Interface input
- General port I/O
- Timing function accurate to milliseconds
- Timing function in microsecond clock ticks
- Sound card access
- Joystick input

The DLL can be used with many programming systems. Due to this, and in this book, any program language can use its functions calls, for example it can be called from C++. The DLL can also be used in Word or Excel macros (see Chapters 1.2 and 14).

The development of a generalised DLL enables access to any hardware and in certain ways is contrary to the Windows philosophy, where all hardware access is under driver control. A driver always applies to a well-known piece of equipment, and for minor hardware experiments, there is actually no requirement for it. Correct driver development is also very complex, so that in practice only large Companies can undertake it. Under DOS and also in other programming languages there are port commands (GWBASIC: INP and OUT, in Turbo Pascal: PORT [..]), and with these one can directly access PC hardware. Under Windows 3.1, the limitations were relatively minor, so that one can easily pass over this. Even Delphi 1 still had the old PORT command.

Under Windows 95, it became more difficult. Visual Basic 5 no longer provides direct access options for the general port addressing. In Delphi 3 direct port access is possible but only using inline assembler coding. Such coding is utilised in the DLL, and general access to the ports is made possible, even in Visual Basic. Though new port commands are provided it is not always possible to use them directly from the operating system. Accordingly, ordinary open commands must be used before anything is done with the corresponding hardware.

# 1 Introduction

Under Windows NT it seems there is no possibility left for the hobbyist developer. The primary aim in Windows NT development was security such that no direct hardware access is permitted. The only route left is the normal way using drivers therefore any new hardware needs to be accessed over the serial interface. In this manner all accesses are also possible under Windows NT as ordinary system calls are used in the DLL.

Generally it must be stressed that this book describes the experimental work with PC interfaces. All introduced programs were developed under Windows 95 and Windows 98 using the 32 bit programming systems, Visual Basic and Delphi 4. There is always a risk that programs may not function correctly on certain computers. For example, an interface could be installed differently on that particular computer, or a new Windows version could be encountered which uses a different way of handling the interfaces. The Reader should never try to develop professional industrial controls using these experimental methods. If this advice is not followed, it could easily happen that the Readers telephone will never stop ringing, with furious callers every day, and the only way left is to escape to a far and lonely island!

## 1.2 Visual Basic 5 DLL calls

Fundamental use of a DLL is firstly demonstrated here with a simple example requiring no additional hardware. The PC loudspeaker is controlled by chips that can be controlled by port commands. It either executes using a timer, with a fixed frequency sound emitted, or is directly controlled by an output port on the PC 8255 PIO chip. In this manner, it is also possible to generate sounds by merely switching a line quickly on and off. This method is introduced here in order to learn the fundamental use of a DLL and also to examine the timing skills of Windows.

The loudspeaker uses one bit of Port B on the 8255. The chip occupies the address 60h (96 decimal) of the PC I/O area, and Port B lies at address 97. Communications are always performed with an 8-bit byte, so all 8 bits are switched simultaneously. However, only the second bit (bit 1) may be changed, as port B of the PIO chip has many other important tasks to execute. Therefore, the actual port state must be read first in order to change only one bit with a new byte output. If the Reader is not familiar with this type of 'bit byting' there is need reason for concern. On the one hand the CD program is ready for use, and on the other hand, many tasks are much easier when using ordinary interfaces such as the COM or Printer port.

For access to the individual PC port addresses the DLL has two special functions (note that upper case must be used for PORT.DLL functions):

```
OUTPORT  - data output from data at an address
INPORT   - read address from an I/O address
```

In Visual Basic, OUTPORT may also be declared as a sub procedure, whilst INPORT must be a function. The individual elements of a DLL are specified with the DECLARE command. Then, for the data exchange between Visual Basic and the DLL to function correctly, parameters must always be declared 'ByVal', that is: a parameter is a value but not a reference address. Under the 32-bit operating system Windows 95/98 accurate spelling of the declaration must be observed. Since all the functions are written in upper case in the DLL, this capitalisation must be observed in the calling program. The declarations must be declare, in a separate Module (here: Module1.bas), which is then bound in the Project SOUND.

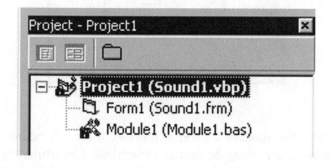

*Fig 1.1*
*Project Sound*

```
Declare Sub OUTPORT Lib "PORT.DLL" (ByVal Adr As Integer,
    ByVal Dat As Integer)
Declare Function INPORT Lib "PORT.DLL" (ByVal Adr As Integer)
    As Integer
Declare Sub DELAY Lib "PORT.DLL" (ByVal Time As Integer)
```

*Listing 1.1*
*Declarations in*
*Module1.bas*

INPORT and OUTPORT are the only functions, which need to be used in the entire Project. Additionally, the Delay procedure is declared, for further applications below. The first Sound sample is generated in a fast loop with 100 impulses of the loudspeaker, and the sound should be clearly heard. The individual bit manipulation of the Port output with 'OUTPORT' utilises the logic functions, AND/ OR, in order to change only one line of the port read before by INPORT. These functions will be further explained below.

The program takes a simple form, making use of a switch button 'Sound'. The load speaker port line is turned on and off 100 times. In order to hear anything at all with a Pentium 200MHz, it is necessary to insert additional delays. These consist of counting loops up to 10 000 in this case.

*Fig 1.2*

*Program*
*window*

When the speaker button is pressed, a tone is heard, with sound accuracy being computer dependent. Unfortunately, the sound wave cannot be described as having great clarity, rather it

```
Private Sub Command1_Click()
   For n = 1 To 100
      OUTPORT 97, (INPORT(97) Or 2)
      For t = 1 To 10000: Next t
      OUTPORT 97, (INPORT(97) And 253)
      For t = 1 To 10000: Next t
   Next n
End Sub
```

*Listing 1.2*
*Loudspeaker*
*output*
*(SOUND.FRM)*

clunks both substantially and scratchily, one can almost say croaky. The reason for this lies in the timing constraints in Windows.

Delays generated by counting loops can never be of the same length because Windows must deal concurrently with many other operations. It must for example observe the mouse, and it must eventually serve parallel processing management. One can say therefore, that Windows is not capable of true real time execution, i.e. it is not possible to control fast processes with acceptable reliability. However, this is relative, and it is worth considering how quick and how reliable control needs to be. Clean sound cannot be expected when the earlier example of program code is used.

Counting loops is not the first choice in delay methods. Windows itself offers better means of generating exact delays in the region of milliseconds. It was due to this that the Delay function of the DLL was made available. The sound can be used to help tune and improve the delay. Unfortunately, the highest frequency

*Listing 1.3*
*Sound output*
*with delay*
*(Sound2.frm)*

```
Private Sub Command1_Click()
   For n = 1 To 100
      OUTPORT 97, (INPORT(97) Or 2)
      DELAY 1
      OUTPORT 97, (INPORT(97) And 253)
      DELAY 1
   Next n
End Sub
```

possible is approximately 500Hz with the port state changing every millisecond.

The generated sound heard is now essentially better, but it is still not so clear as if it were a pure electronic generation. As a consequence the DLL procedure RealTime (true) is used for essential improvement (see Chap 3.2). A rough impression can be gained from this of how wide the real time capability in Windows can be. Accurate examination can be made using an oscilloscope. However, for that to be possible in the earlier program, the interface must be changed, for example, to the serial COM port.

Besides a millisecond delay function in the DLL there is a delay in micro seconds. This function also uses internal Windows calls.

*Listing 1.4*
*Module*
*PORTS.BAS*
*with VB5*
*declarations*

All DLL calls are declared in a single external Basic module PORTS.BAS, which can be loaded trouble free in each new Project. Without it, the accurate declaration convention would remain a concern, but the programmer has from now on, access to all DLL functions. PORT.DLL must be bound with the compiled user pro-

```
Declare Function OPENCOM Lib "Port" (ByVal A$) As Integer
Declare Sub CLOSECOM Lib "Port" ()
Declare Sub SENDBYTE Lib "Port" (ByVal b%)
Declare Function READBYTE Lib "Port" () As Integer
Declare Sub DTR Lib "Port" (ByVal b%)
Declare Sub RTS Lib "Port" (ByVal b%)
Declare Sub TXD Lib "Port" (ByVal b%)
Declare Function CTS Lib "Port" () As Integer
Declare Function DSR Lib "Port" () As Integer
Declare Function RI Lib "Port" () As Integer
Declare Function DCD Lib "Port" () As Integer
Declare Sub DELAY Lib "Port" (ByVal b%)
Declare Sub TIMEINIT Lib "Port" ()
Declare Sub TIMEINITUS Lib "Port" ()
Declare Function TIMEREAD Lib "Port" () As Long
Declare Function TIMEREADUS Lib "Port" () As Long
```

***continued on following page ...***

```
Declare Sub DELAYUS Lib "Port" (ByVal l As Long)
Declare Sub REALTIME Lib "Port" (ByVal i As Boolean)
Declare Sub OUTPORT Lib "Port" (ByVal A%, ByVal b%)
Declare Function INPORT Lib "Port" (ByVal p%) As Integer
Declare Function JOYX Lib "Port" () As Long
Declare Function JOYY Lib "Port" () As Long
Declare Function JOYZ Lib "Port" () As Long
Declare Function JOYW Lib "Port" () As Long
Declare Function JOYBUTTON Lib "Port" () As Integer
Declare Function SOUNDSETRATE Lib "Port" (ByVal Rate%)
     As Integer
Declare Function SOUNDGETRATE Lib "Port" () As Integer
Declare Function SOUNDBUSY Lib "Port" () As Boolean
Declare Function SOUNDIS Lib "Port" () As Boolean
Declare Sub SOUNDIN Lib "Port" (ByVal Buffer$, ByVal Size%)
Declare Sub SOUNDOUT Lib "Port" (ByVal Buffer$, ByVal Size%)
Declare Function SOUNDGETBYTES Lib "Port" () As Integer
Declare Function SOUNDSETBYTES Lib "Port" (ByVal b%)
     As Integer
Declare Sub SOUNDCAPIN Lib "Port" ()
Declare Sub SOUNDCAPOUT Lib "Port" ()
```

gram, either via., the Windows-directory or in the compilation directory of the .exe program.

In a similar way the DLL functions can also reside in a VBA declaration. One can also in principal, perform all experiments in this book using Word or Excel. The program resides in a macro, which is started directly from the application. In Word 7 and Excel 7 the declarations are as in Visual Basic 5. The following example of sound generation with the PC loud speaker was devised with Word 97 and further VBA examples can be found in Chapter14.

In Word97 a macro can also be used, utilising a User-Form, containing control elements. The keyword 'Private' must be used together with 'Declare' and all functions and procedures must also be declared 'Private' (see figure on following page).

*Fig 1.3*
*A Word97 macro*

## 1.3 Delphi DLL Calls

In Delphi 4 all port accesses are also made via. PORT.DLL. The first example is a simple sound generator using the PC load speaker. The program contains two switch buttons for sound generation, one (Sound1) with a delay loop and one (Sound2) operated with the DLL procedure DELAY.

*Fig 1.4*
*First Delphi program*

The DLL expansions are declared in the same unit like normal procedures or functions but instead of program code they are linked to the external DLL. The keywords 'stdcall' and 'external', control the handing over of parameters to the DLL and are essential for a correct output.

Also important is the choice of appropriate variable types for parameter passing. Delphi itself has documented, that the structure of type Integer is no longer compatible between the individual versions. It is possible then, that in each version problems are generated when one uses a source file from Delphi 3 in Delphi 4, or the opposite. There is no problem with the type Word (16 bit unsigned) and DWord (32 bit unsigned) as well as Real.

The Delphi Unit (*.pas), cannot use the same name as the project (*.dpr) (this is a Delphi constraint). In this book the suffix P has been used throughout for 'Project' and the Project file names follows the same convention. The file SOUND1.pas is given the project name SOUND1P.dpr, and after compilation the exported program, SOUND1P.exe is generated.

*Listing 1.5*
*Sound output*
*in Delphi*
*(Sound1.pas)*

```
unit Sound1;

interface

uses
   Windows, Messages, SysUtils, Classes, Graphics,
   Controls, Forms, Dialogs, StdCtrls;

type
  TForm1 = class(TForm)
     Sound1: TButton; Sound2: TButton;
     procedure Sound1Click(Sender: TObject);
     procedure Sound2Click(Sender: TObject);
  end;

var
   Form1: TForm1;
```

*continued on following page ...*

# 1 Introduction

```
implementation

{$R *.DFM}

procedure OUTPORT (adr: Word; Value: Word);
    stdcall; external 'PORT.dll';

function INPORT (adr: Word):Integer;
    stdcall; external 'PORT.DLL';

procedure DELAY (ms: Word);
    stdcall; external 'PORT.DLL';

procedure TForm1.Sound1Click(Sender: TObject);
var n, t: Integer;
begin
  For n := 1 to 100 do begin
    OutPort (97, (InPort (97) OR 2));
    For t := 1 to 10000 Do;
    OutPort (97, (InPort (97) AND 253));
    For t := 1 to 10000 Do;
  end;
end;

procedure TForm1.Sound2Click(Sender: TObject);
var n: Integer;
begin
  For n := 1 to 100 do begin
    OutPort (97, (InPort (97) OR 2));
    Delay (1);
    OutPort (97, (InPort (97) AND 253));
    Delay (1);
  end;
end;

end.
```

On choosing a time delay loop, it will be apparent that Delphi gives a 10 times greater performance speed compared to Visual Basic. With a 200 MHz PC one finds a frequency of approximately. 5kHz for a counting loop of 10 000. With faster computers, the sound is virtually outside the audible spectrum.

Many applications need a reliable time control which is independent of the actual computer. The delay procedure in principle produces the same time behaviour in every environment. A single click on button 'Sound1' generates a constant sound of 500Hz, on the basis of the Delay procedure.

In Delphi it is also sensible that all declarations of the DLL are inserted in the same Module, which is a Unit in Delphi. The unit PORTINC.pas (in compiled form PORTINC.dcu) can be bound in each new Project, so there is no longer any concern with individual declaration conventions.

*Listing 1.6*
*PORT.DLL*
*declarations*
*in the file*
*PORTINC.PAS*

```
unit PORTINC;

interface

uses windows;

const THEDLL='PORT.DLL';
Procedure DELAY(i:WORD); stdcall; external THEDLL;
Procedure TIMEINIT; stdcall; external THEDLL;
Function TIMEREAD: DWORD; stdcall; external THEDLL;
Procedure DELAYUS(i:DWORD); stdcall; external THEDLL;
Procedure TIMEINITUS; stdcall; external THEDLL;
Function TIMEREADUS: DWORD; stdcall; external THEDLL;
Procedure OUTPORT(PortAddr:Word; Data:byte); stdcall;
     external THEDLL;
Function INPORT(PortAddr:Word):Byte;stdcall; external THEDLL;
Function OPENCOM(S:PCHAR):Integer;stdcall; external THEDLL;
Function READBYTE:Integer;stdcall; external THEDLL;
```

***continued on following page ...***

# 1 Introduction

```
Procedure SENDBYTE(d:WORD);stdcall; external THEDLL;
Procedure DTR(d:WORD);stdcall; external THEDLL;
Procedure RTS(d:WORD);stdcall; external THEDLL;
Procedure TXD(d:WORD);stdcall; external THEDLL;
Function CTS:Integer;stdcall; external THEDLL;
Function DSR:Integer;stdcall; external THEDLL;
Function RI:Integer;stdcall; external THEDLL;
Function DCD:Integer;stdcall; external THEDLL;
Procedure REALTIME(d:BOOLEAN);stdcall; external THEDLL;
Function SOUNDSETRATE(Rate:DWORD):DWORD; stdcall;
      external THEDLL;
Function SOUNDGETRATE:DWORD; stdcall; external THEDLL;
Function SOUNDBUSY:Boolean; stdcall; external THEDLL;
Function SOUNDIS:Boolean; stdcall; external THEDLL;
Procedure SOUNDIN(Buffer:Pchar;Size:DWORD); stdcall;
      external THEDLL;
Procedure SOUNDOUT(Buffer:Pchar;Size:DWORD); stdcall;
      external THEDLL;
Function SOUNDGETBYTES:DWORD; stdcall; external THEDLL;
Function SOUNDSETBYTES(B:DWORD):DWORD; stdcall;
      external THEDLL;
Procedure SOUNDCAPIN; stdcall; external THEDLL;
Procedure SOUNDCAPOUT; stdcall; external THEDLL;
Function JOYX:DWORD;stdcall; external THEDLL;
Function JOYY:DWORD;stdcall; external THEDLL;
Function JOYZ:DWORD;stdcall; external THEDLL;
Function JOYR:DWORD;stdcall; external THEDLL;
Function JOYBUTTON:DWORD;stdcall; external THEDLL;

implementation

end.
```

**2**

# Serial Interface

Every PC has one or more serial interfaces, which in the manuals are usually designated COM1, COM2 et seq. Their original intended purpose was the interconnection between computer and modem for data exchange over a telephone network. Many times however, other equipment, such as a printer, mouse or serial measuring devices are also connected. Therefore, additional serial interfaces are often used side by side in the PC.

The serial interface also provides numerous advantages for simple experiments, because:

- The serial interface is very robust with regard to inadvertent destruction.
- Equipment may be connected or disconnected while the PC is running.
- For simple equipment, power can be supplied from the serial interface.

When conversion of serially transmitted data into parallel data is required, the serial interface often invokes an increased overhead. For minor tasks, with only a few I/O lines however, the directly connected auxiliary lines of the serial interface can be used. Altogether there are three output connections and five input connections, which when combined with simple instructions, permit direct communication.

The table on the following page shows the pin-out of 25-way and 9-way D-type plugs. The male plugs are always on the PC side, so the port connectors in Figure2.1 must be female.

## 2  Serial Interface

| Pin 25-way | Pin 9-way | Input/ Output | Label | Function |
|---|---|---|---|---|
| 2 | 3 | Out | TXD | Transmit Data |
| 3 | 2 | In | RXD | Receive Data |
| 4 | 7 | Out | RTS | Request To Send |
| 5 | 8 | In | CTS | Clear To Send |
| 6 | 6 | In | DSR | Data Set Ready |
| 7 | 5 | | GND | Ground |
| 8 | 1 | In | DCD | Data Carrier Detect |
| 20 | 4 | Out | DTR | Data Terminal Ready |
| 22 | 9 | In | RI | Ring Indicator |

*Figure 2.1*

*25-way and 9-way D-type port connectors (solder side)*

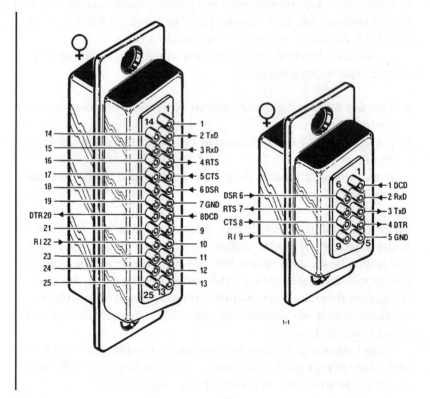

Data transmission via the serial interface normally occurs on the serial transmit line TxD and the serial receive line RxD. All spare lines have auxiliary functions associated with the protocol and the control of the data transmission. They are usually classified as 'handshake' lines, and are used for acknowledging operations between equipment. The specific advantage of the handshake lines is that their status can be directly set or read.

The electrical properties of the I/O lines are specified in the RS232 standard.In the low state –12 V is specified, and in high state +12V. All outputs are short-circuit proof and can sink or source up to some 10 to 20mA. With that capacity, LED's can be illuminated, or driver interfaces can be directly controlled. As a result, it is possible to power relatively small circuits directly from the serial interface outputs.

The input resistances are approximately 10 kΩ and interpret a voltage greater than approximately 1.25 V as high, while a low is detected for an input voltage under 1.0 V. Transient noise can cause continuous voltage fluctuations between these limits (switch hysteresis effect), and this cannot be permitted to trigger a false switch. Accordingly a voltage of say 1.1 V, is undefined and cannot be regarded as either high or low. The switch status only changes when the voltage lies outside the 1.25 V to 1.0 V range.

Normally the serial interface is driven by bipolar signal levels at +12 V and –12 V. As the usual input circuitry in the PC reads a voltage below 1 V as low, it is also possible to work with TTL levels (0 V / 5 V). However, some PC's, mostly laptops, work with switching thresholds of circa –3 V and +3 V, and thus must use bipolar input signals.

## 2.1 Serial Interface DLL functions

PORT.DLL contains numerous functions for direct control of the serial interface lines. These calls have been written by the authors and can be regarded as an API superset, with the parameters and functions specified. Such calls can be made available under Windows by copying PORT.DLL into the Windows directory. Using the OpenCom function, the system and the DLL must first of all communicate, and determine which COM interface is to be used. Windows will refuse access if a COM port is already assigned. It is then possible for three lines to be switched and four lines to be directly read. Also, in a simple manner, the DLL can be used for serial data transmission and reception.

The following is a summary of the available functions:

*Interface opening and closing:*
- OpenCOM (parameter)
- CloseCOM

*Single bytes – sending and receiving:*
- SendByte
- ReadByte

*Direct output using serial interface lines:*
- DTR
- RTS
- TXD

*Reading the port lines :*
- CTS
- DSR
- RI
- DCD

None of these calls utilise direct port access; instead, they are Windows functions, so they also still function under Windows NT. They should therefore be used whenever possible instead of direct hardware access using port commands.

## 2.2 RS232 access in Visual Basic

Visual Basic is suitable for small programs, but the shortest code execution time does not result from this high level language. The first small application example is the direct control of an LED over the DTR line (see Figure 2.2). Only in this case may the LED be used without any additional series resistor, as all outputs of the serial interface are current limited to a maximum of circa 10 to 20 mA.

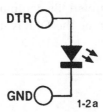

*Figure 2.2*
*Light-emitting*
*diode on the*
*serial interface*

The Blinker program uses the Visual Basic timer. The blinking speed is defined by the property 'interval' of the timers, which is initially declared during programming but can also be changed at run time. The timer is not very accurate, but is acceptable for a Blinker. The program uses a slider control bar for setting the blinking speed. It can be set incrementally from zero to 1000 cycles per second, using a 1000 ms timer interval.

The program uses the declaration in the Project Module PORTS.BAS. The OpenCOM function is used here to open the COM2 interface, and only after opening does the DLL know which COM interface line is to be addressed. In the event the COM interface is already occupied by another Program, an error message is

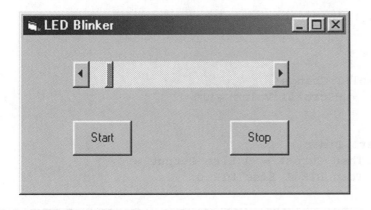

*Figure 2.3*
*LED Blinker*
*program*

simultaneously received. In Visual Basic the interface must always be closed at Program exit (Form_Unload) with CloseCOM, because Visual Basic does not terminate or unload the DLL from memory. Failing this, at the next program start, the COM interface may still be found occupied. By comparison, in Delphi the Close can be dispensed with, as the DLL is unloaded at EXE program termination.

**Listing 2.1**

*An LED blinker (BLINK.FRM)*

```
Dim Output As Integer

Private Sub Command1_Click()
   Timer1.Interval = HScroll1.Value + 10
   Timer1.Enabled = True
End Sub

Private Sub Command2_Click()
   Timer1.Enabled = False
End Sub

Private Sub Form_Load()
 i = OPENCOM("COM2,1200,N,8,1")
 If i = 0 Then MsgBox ("COM Port unavailable")
 Timer1.Interval = 250
 Timer1.Enabled = True
 Output = 0
End Sub

Private Sub Form_Unload(Cancel As Integer)
CLOSECOM
End Sub

Private Sub HScroll1_Change()
 Timer1.Interval = HScroll1.Value + 10
End Sub

Private Sub Timer1_Timer()
   If Output = 1 Then Output = 0 Else Output = 1
   If Output = 1 Then DTR 1 Else DTR 0
End Sub
```

With each call of the timer procedure the DTR line status is changed. Accordingly, the global Variable OUTPUT was used, and dependent on its value, DTR was then set or re-set. The blinking can be switched off by using the switch area 'Stop', the timer then halts.

The second example shows, how a simple switch can be read using the Computer. The switch makes contact, for example between the high state output line RTS and the input line CTS (see Figure 2.4). The program QUERY.FRM initialises the three available output lines to high, interrogates all inputs at regular intervals and provides the status in the check boxes. The interrogation is again controlled using the timer.

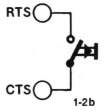

*Figure 2.4*
*Switch*
*connections*
*on the serial*
*interface*

*Figure 2.5*
*Status report for*
*all input lines*

**Listing 2.2** *Input states reported on the screen*

```
Private Sub Form_Load()
 i = OPENCOM("COM2,1200,N,8,1")
 If i = 0 Then
     i = OPENCOM("COM1,1200,N,8,1")
     Option1.Value = True
 End If
 If i = 0 Then MsgBox ("COM Port unavailable")
 TXD 1
 RTS 1
 DTR 1
 TIMEINIT
End Sub


Private Sub Form_Unload(Cancel As Integer)
   CLOSECOM
End Sub
Private Sub Option1_Click()
 i = OPENCOM("COM1,1200,N,8,1")
 If i = 0 Then MsgBox ("COM Port unavailable ")
 TXD 1
 RTS 1
 DTR 1
End Sub


Private Sub Option2_Click()
 i = OPENCOM("COM2,1200,N,8,1")
 If i = 0 Then MsgBox ("COM Port unavailable ")
 TXD 1
 RTS 1
 DTR 1
End Sub


Private Sub Timer1_Timer()
   If CTS() = 1 Then Check1.Value = 1 Else Check1.Value = 0
   If DSR() = 1 Then Check2.Value = 1 Else Check2.Value = 0
   If DCD() = 1 Then Check3.Value = 1 Else Check3.Value = 0
   If RI() = 1 Then Check4.Value = 1 Else Check4.Value = 0
End Sub
```

This program demonstrates a better procedure for serial interface selection. Instead of any specific interface, first preference was sought here, automatically, i.e. COM1 to open, in the event COM2 being busy and COM2 is opened by default. In the event COM2 is occupied with the mouse, COM1 will be used. The User can also change the COM interface with a mouse click. In the event there are two free interfaces, and altogether up to eight switches can be interrogated. For many cases in this book, these operations can be bound in front of the program, and it is also easy to expand up to four serial interfaces.

After program shut down, the serial interface is closed with CloseCOM. This is especially important in the experimental exercise with Visual Basic, because the DLL is not automatically unloaded from memory at program shut down, but controlled by the development language VB5. If the CloseCOM call is forgotten in the procedure Form_Unload, then, another program will find the interface is occupied, as reported by the Open command. It is completely different in Delphi where a complete EXE file is always generated. When the DLL is shut down it is completely unloaded from memory, and with that the interface released.

## 2.3  RS232 access in Delphi

Delphi programming is capable of solving time-critical problems. The source text is first compiled into binary code, i.e., machine code, for very fast program execution. The programming effort is much greater than in Visual Basic. Application writers, with work experience of Pascal, will find in Delphi a genuine alternative.

The first programming example is to solve a comparable exercise with the Visual Basic program in Listing 2.1. Again an output line is controlled as per Figure 2.2. Before output line access, the interface must be opened. The correct interface number is important, whilst other Parameters like Baud Rate. Parity etc. are here, set arbitrarily. Per C convention, the Open String must be passed to the DLL with a null termination. Parameters shown in the declaration of the OPENCOM function use the Pascal type PCHAR.

```
Function OPENCOM(S:PCHAR):Integer; stdcall; external
      ´PORT.DLL´;
OpenCom (Pchar('COM2:9600,N,8,1'));
```

*Figure 2.6*

*Rectangular
waveform
generator with
adjustable
edge length*

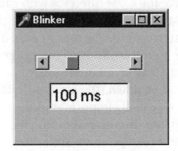

All declarations are already made in the Unit PORTINC.PAS
(see Chapter 1.3). The Unit is inserted into the Project by the USES
statement.

*Listing 2.3*

*Clock generator
in Delphi*

```
unit Blinker;

interface

uses PortInc, Windows, Messages, SysUtils, Classes,
   Graphics, Controls, Forms, Dialogs, ExtCtrls, StdCtrls;

type
  TForm1 = class(TForm)
    ScrollBar1: TScrollBar; Edit1: TEdit;
    Timer1: TTimer;
    procedure ScrollBar1Change(Sender: TObject);
    procedure FormCreate(Sender: TObject);
    procedure Timer1Timer(Sender: TObject);
  end;
```

*continued on following page ...*

```
var
  Form1: TForm1;

implementation

{$R *.DFM}

var Output: Integer;

procedure TForm1.ScrollBar1Change(Sender: TObject);
begin
  Edit1.Text := floattostr(Scrollbar1.Position)+ ' ms';
  Timer1.Interval := Scrollbar1.Position
end;

procedure TForm1.FormCreate(Sender: TObject);
begin
  OpenCom (Pchar('COM2:9600,N,8,1'));
  Timer1.Enabled := true;
  Output := 0;
end;

procedure TForm1.Timer1Timer(Sender: TObject);
begin
  Output := (Output + 1) AND 1;
  DTR (Output);
  RTS (Output);
end;

end.
```

The program BLINKER controls the DTR and RTS lines using symmetrical rectangular signals. The impulse length is adjustable using a slider control and is controlled via Timer1. Measurement shows, that the Timer generates reliable time intervals no shorter than 50 ms. The slider is defined by the properties 'Min' and 'Max' of the ScrollBar1 with limits of 50 ms and 250 ms.

The second example is the interrogation of switches status. The program first of all reads and stores 2000 switch status values and then writes them immediately on the screen. The time between the Port interrogations at 100 µsec is so small, that contact bounce can be identified. The program uses a 'Memo input field' for presentation of the zero and ones values on the screen.

*Figure 2.7*

*The result of fast switch interrogation*

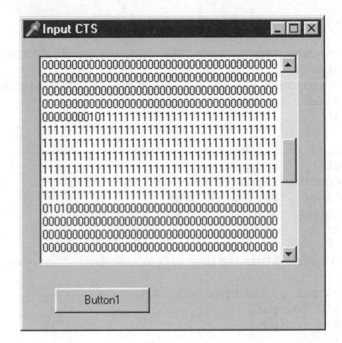

*Listing 2.4*

*Switch interrogation in Pascal*

```
unit Switch;

interface

uses  PortInc,Windows, Messages, SysUtils, Classes,
  Graphics, Controls, Forms, Dialogs, StdCtrls;
```

***continued on following page . . .***

```
type
  TForm1 = class(TForm)
    Memo1: TMemo;    Button1: TButton;
    procedure Button1Click(Sender: TObject);
    procedure FormCreate(Sender: TObject);
  end;

var
  Form1: TForm1;

implementation

{$R *.DFM}

procedure TForm1.Button1Click(Sender: TObject);
var Buffer: Array [0..2000] of Byte;
    n, m: Integer;
    Value: String;
begin
  for n:= 0 to 2000 do begin
    Buffer[n]:=CTS;
    Delayus(100);
  end;
  For n:= 0 to 49 do begin
    Value := '';
    For m:= 0 to 39 do begin
      Value := Value + floattostr(Buffer[40*n+m]);
    end;
    Memo1.Lines[n]:=Value;
  end;
end;

procedure TForm1.FormCreate(Sender: TObject);
begin
  OpenCom (Pchar('COM2:9600,N,8,1'));
  DTR (1); RTS(1);
end;

end.
```

Accurate examination of the time delays, for example with a function generator on the CTS input shows, that the time delay of 100 µs cannot be reliably maintained. Many time gaps can be found, this being caused by Windows itself. It is shown below, how the timing reliability can be increased with a DLL call RealTime(True).

## 2.4  Access using port commands

PC serial interfaces use the  National Semiconductor 8250 UART ('UART' stands for 'Universal Asynchronous Receiver / Transmitter'), the successor type 16450, or a compatible type. This UART contains 10 registers, with which all functions of serial I/O can be controlled. The chip has seven addresses assigned, some of which use a double allocation. The following table shows all the 8250 registers, only a few of which are utilised in this book.

Each of these registers comprise an eight bit byte, and there are therefore eight individual memory cells for particular functions. It is not possible to explain all of these functions in the present text. Especially important for the following chapters, and for

| Register | Offset | Comments |
| --- | --- | --- |
| Receive buffer register | 0 | read only |
| Transmit buffer register | 0 | write only |
| Only accessible when bit 7 of line control register is high: | | |
| Baud rate register (low) | 0 | low byte of baud rate |
| Baud rate register (high) | 1 | high byte of baud rate |
| Interrupt enable register | 1 | IER |
| Interrupt identification register | 2 | IIR (read only) |
| Line control register | 3 | LCR |
| Modem control register | 4 | MCR |
| Line status register | 5 | LSR |
| Modem status register | 6 | MSR |
| Scratch register | 7 | SCR |

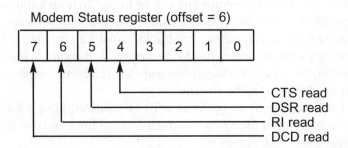

Modem Status register (offset = 6)

CTS read
DSR read
RI read
DCD read

writing of simple interface applications, are the Modem-control register and the Modem-Status register, which provide access to the interface auxiliary lines.

All registers are handled in the PC's I/O memory region. The computer finds register addresses in this region at a fixed memory location for each interface, with the first address being the base address (BA) shown below. The first serial interface (COM1) uses the base address 3F8 (hexadecimal). This register occupies the memory range 3F8 to 3FF (i.e. 8 bytes long). The offset of a register address is then the offset previously indicated.

All programs in this book use the second serial interface (COM2), but with a modified base address, they can also be used with COM1 through COM4. Addresses are generally written in hexadecimal format throughout, but decimal equivalents are also permissible. Base addresses for the individual COM interfaces are given in the following table.

|             | COM1 | COM2 | COM3 | COM4 |
|-------------|------|------|------|------|
| hexadecimal | 3F8  | 2F8  | 3E8  | 2E8  |
| decimal     | 1016 | 760  | 1000 | 744  |

Under Windows 95/98 all device properties of the COM interface are accessible from the control panel on the System Control / System / Device Manager/ Port Control tab. For each interface under the Device Manager 'Resources' tab, the address location and the associated interrupt line can be found. In individual cases when additional COM interfaces are registered in other ways the absolute address can differ from the information given here. This is not a problem, when hardware access is through Windows. However, for an access directly through the Hardware register, the correct address must be ensured.

Direct access to a register is at its absolute address, which is the summation of the COM interface Base address and the UART register offset, calculated as:

base address + offset = register address

If for example, the first serial interface is controlled using the auxiliary lines DTR and RTS, the addresses (3F8+4) and 3FC must be accessed. It is noteworthy; the Base address BA is only defined once in the program. The target address (BA+4) can then be used independently of the COMn interface.

Direct output over DTR and RTS lines use the address (BA+4), so for COM1 the address is 1020 (3FC):

| Modem Control Register | | |
|---|---|---|
| **Address** | **Bit** | **Port** |
| BA+4 | 0 | DTR |
| BA+4 | 1 | RTS |

*Example:* The RTS line is to be switched on: bit 1 is addressed with the numerical value $2^1 = 2$, therefore a 2 is output. The word $2^0 = 1$ corresponds to DTR being turned on, and the word 3 both lines (i.e. $2^0 + 2^1 = 3$). Using the OutPort-function of PORT.DLL the coding syntax in VB and Delphi looks like:

```
in Visual Basic:    OutPort BA+4, 2   : REM RTS on
in Delphi:          OutPort (BA+4,2)  ; (RTS on)
```

The reader may be disappointed if a direct port output in Visual Basic 5 or in Delphi 4 is used: OutPort is executed without any warning message, but the output is not actually sent to any level switch on the RTS line.

The problem lies with the General Protection mechanism of Windows. In accordance with this, an array is written to memory for all Port addresses, but the output is not transmitted to the real hardware. First of all, system permission must be gained for any access request. This is executed through a COM interface opening in accordance with the API rules, in a simple case with the OpenCOM function of the DLL. Windows provides feedback of success or failure, for example when a COM interface does not exist, or is occupied by another program.

At least Windows 95 still provides another, though not wholly clean method: the COM interface can be removed from the system with the help of Device Manager. It is then no longer supervised and can be arbitrarily utilised. The operation does make sense however, when one spare interface will be used exclusively for simple hardware experiments. In contrast, a more practical and efficient way is the application of OpenCOM. The program shown in Listing 2.5 generates a square wave impulse on the RTS line of the COM2 interface. A 500-Hz signal will be seen at this port. The COM interface is opened with OpenCOM when the program starts. Direct input via the CTS, DSR, RI and DCD lines is executed at address (BA+6), so for COM2 this is at the address 766 (2FE), as shown in the table following Listing 2.5.

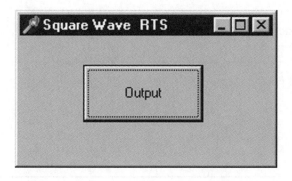

*Figure 2.8*
*Direct output*
*on RTS*

# 2 Serial Interface

*Listing 2.5* *COM Interface opening and control*

```
unit Rectangular;

interface

uses PortInc,Windows, Messages, SysUtils, Classes,
   Graphics, Controls, Forms, Dialogs, ExtCtrls, StdCtrls;

type
  TForm1 = class(TForm)
    Button1: TButton;
    procedure FormCreate(Sender: TObject);
    procedure Button1Click(Sender: TObject);
  end;

var
  Form1: TForm1;

implementation

{$R *.DFM}

Const BA = $02F8;
procedure TForm1.FormCreate(Sender: TObject);
begin
  OpenCom (Pchar('COM2:9600,N,8,1'));
end;

procedure TForm1.Button1Click(Sender: TObject);
var n: Integer;
begin
  For n := 1 to 100 do begin
    OutPort (BA+4, 2);
    Delay (1);
    OutPort (BA+4, 0);
    Delay (1);
  end;
end;

end.
```

| Modem Status register | | | |
|---|---|---|---|
| **Address** | **Bit** | **Port** | **Value** |
| BA+6 | 4 | CTS | 16 |
| BA+6 | 5 | DSR | 32 |
| BA+6 | 6 | RI | 64 |
| BA+6 | 7 | DCD | 128 |

*Example:* the CTS line is interrogated: Bit 4 represents the numerical value $2^4 = 16$. With this fact and with a Port command in which all eight bits of the registers have been mutually read, a known bit can be isolated ( masked ) with the AND-function. The function AND 16 results in all the other bits being reset, so that the result is either 16 (CTS on) or 0 (CTS off):

```
if (InPort (BA+6) AND 16) = 16 then .....
```

While four input lines are available, only two outputs are available on the serial interface auxiliary line. When that is insufficient, the serial send line TxD can also be directly controlled. The output TxD is normally used for asynchronous data transmission. The so called Break state was originally used to simulate a signal line break, however it can also be directly switched on. For this to function, bit 6 of the Line Control register must be set.

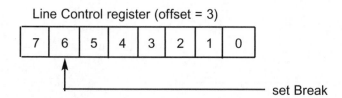

Line Control register (offset = 3)

| 7 | 6 | 5 | 4 | 3 | 2 | 1 | 0 |

set Break

If TxD is to be switched on, then 64 must be written to the address (BA+3). The output will only succeed, if the COM interface has already been opened. In Visual Basic this requires the following code:

```
i = OPENCOM ( "COM2, 1200, n, 8, 1" )
If i=0 then MsgBox ( "COM2 unavailable")
BA = 760
OutPort (BA+3), 64
```

In other words, the base address is COM2 at 2F8 (760 decimal) and the Line Control register is seeded with $2^6 = 64$, which issues a simulated break.

In contrast to direct access via hardware addresses, PORT.DLL is a simple alternative, with its output functions DTR, RTS and TXD as well as the read functions CTS, DR, RI and DCD. In many cases direct Port commands can be dispensed with. However, when many simultaneous lines are required with exclusive read access, then this can only succeed with the Port command. Besides this, access to devices such as the Parallel interface or the system hardware timer can be utilised, although these were not considered in the DLL.

# Direct Digital Outputs

The three serial port lines RTS, DTR and TxD can be used for direct control and require only one instruction per output. This permits control of very accurately timed status changes, and interesting applications are apparent, when the internal PC clock timing control is used.

When events must be generated at predefined times, using for example, Visual Basic or Delphi, the PC real-time clock can be used for time control accurate to the second. However, certain jobs require much finer control, in the millisecond or microsecond range, and for these cases Windows offers suitable timers.

## 3.1 Timer clock

The serial interface output connections can sink or source approximately10 mA, and with that capacity, they are capable of easily controlling various power switches. Figure 3.1 (overleaf) shows a possible controller for high-power devices.

Transistors offer the lowest cost for low voltage circuits. However, if devices are to be controlled at mains voltage levels, care must be taken to separate the potentials and ensure isolation. This can be done with conventional relays or the purely electronic alternative, a semiconductor relay, i.e. an optocoupler with triac output. The Sharp S201–D02 has a maximum drive current of 10 mA and can switch loads up to 1.2 A. It contains a zero-crossing switch, so the triac always switches at zero-voltage crossing, so that virtually no radio frequency interference is generated.

*Figure 3.1*

*Controlling
large devices
with power
switches*

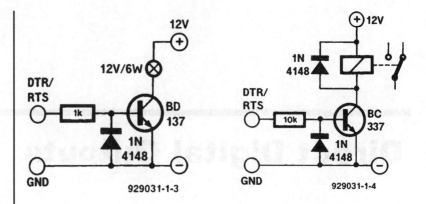

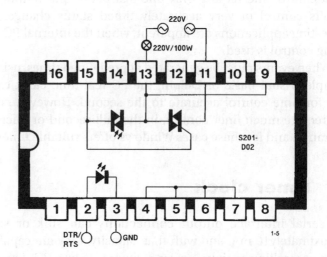

When two semiconductor relays are integrated in an isolated package with two built in sockets, then the PC can be used to develop an intelligent and universal input switch for two independent devices. Possible user applications are numerous, from automatic battery charging to light control for an aquarium.

It is very simple to generate a timing clock in VB5. Figure 3.2 shows the format of a suitable input window, which is described on a 'form', as defined by a Microsoft Visual Basic expression. Using five text boxes, the real time clock and the individual event

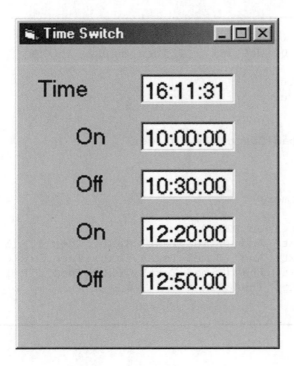

*Figure 3.2*
*Timer*

times are displayed. The switching times can be edited in the VB form at run time. The User can set two clock times for switching on and two for turning off, such that two daily switch cycles are possible. Times must be input in chronological order as shown. The program is limited, but is easily expanded to accommodate further switch points.

Listing 3.1 (overleaf) shows the program text for the time-dependent control of external devices such as lighting. Direct comparison between the real-time clock Time$ and the displayed times in the text box result in changes to the DTR state. The program is controlled by a timer, using an incremental interval of 1000 ms, and every second a new time output and a comparison is made.

The timer switch works problem free in the background. You can thus start the program and then dedicate your attention to other applications.

```
Private Sub Form_Load()
   If OPENCOM("COM2:9600,N,8,1") = 0 Then MsgBox ("COM2
      unavailable")
   Timer1.Interval = 1000
   Timer1.Enabled = True
End Sub

Private Sub Form_Unload(Cancel As Integer)
   CLOSECOM
End Sub

Private Sub Timer1_Timer()
   Text1.Text = Time$
   If Time$<Text1.Text Then DTR 0
   If (Time$>Text2.Text) And (Time$<Text3.Text) Then DTR 1
   If (Time$>Text3.Text) And (Time$<Text4.Text) Then DTR 0
   If (Time$>Text4.Text) And (Time$<Text5.Text) Then DTR 1
   If (Time$>Text5.Text) Then DTR 0
End Sub
```

**Listing 3.1**
*Simple
time switch
program*

## 3.2 Driving servos

Remote-control servos are driven using a series of short pulses with lengths between 1 ms and 2 ms. The pulse repetition frequency is normally approximately 50 Hz, but this is not critical. If not further pulses arrive, the servo maintains its current position. The PC can generate such pulses directly, so that using TxD, RTS and DTR lines, three servos can be controlled. It is then possible to build a programmable movement control model, without great hardware expenditure. Figure 3.3 shows the servo connections to the DTR output, with a Zener diode protecting the inputs from excessive e RS232 voltages.

For accurate time generation with shorter pulses it is necessary to incorporate compiled code. Delphi is fast enough to generate pulses of about 0.1 ms with a microsecond resolution. For time control the procedure 'Delayus' can be used for time delay in

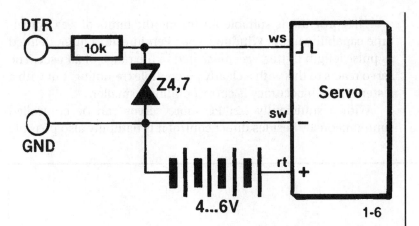

*Figure 3.3*
*Servo control*
*over the serial*
*interface*

a microsecond period. How accurate any time control is, depends mainly on the kind of PC being used. For the first experiment a direct servo control with a Windows slider bar was desired, and Figure 3.4 shows the appearance of the program.

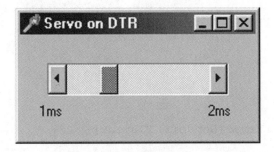

*Figure 3.4*
*Generating the*
*control pulse*
*for a servo*

Listing 3.2 shows one possible solution, the pulse duration of 20 ms being controlled by a timer. Each individual pulse period is controlled by the actual position of the slider control ScrollBar1. The time value is passed into to the procedure Delayus which leads to a pulse of between 1000 µsec and 2000 µsec. The reliability of time measurement speed is increased by switching to RealTime mode.

# 3 Direct Digital Outputs

This program is suitable for testing the limits of a PC's real-time capability under Windows. On a Pentium 75, a jitter, defined as pulse length flutter, was measured in the range of 20 μsec. The servo reacts to this with a clearly perceptible trembling, but with a faster PC the inaccuracy is correspondingly smaller.

With a sufficiently fast PC more servos can be controlled simultaneously. Besides direct control it is naturally also possible

*Listing 3.2*
*Controlling a remote-control servo*

```
unit Servo1;

interface

uses    PORTINC, Windows, Messages, SysUtils, Classes,
   Graphics, Controls, Forms, Dialogs,  ExtCtrls, StdCtrls;

type
   TForm1 = class(TForm)
      ScrollBar1: TScrollBar;   Timer1: TTimer;
      Label1: TLabel;   Label2: TLabel;
      procedure Timer1Timer(Sender: TObject);
      procedure FormCreate(Sender: TObject);
end;

var
   Form1: TForm1;

implementation

{$R *.DFM}

procedure TForm1.Timer1Timer(Sender: TObject);
var PulseTime: Word;
begin
 PulseTime := ScrollBar1.Position;
 RealTime (true);
 DTR (1);
 Delayus (PulseTime);
 DTR (0);
 RealTime (false);
end;
```

*continued on following page ...*

```
procedure TForm1.FormCreate(Sender: TObject);
begin
  OpenCom (Pchar('COM2:9600,N,8,1'));
  Timer1.Interval := 20;
  Timer1.Enabled := true;
end;

end.
```

to generate, automatic movement outputs. The following program demonstrates control of two servos from DTR and RTS, and here the X and Y positions of an imaginary machine are finely adjusted. Using a slow sine and cosine control positioning, a circular movement generator can be built with mechanical correlation.

The program makes use of two timers, with Timer1 controlling the pulse repetition time, and Timer2 the actual movement. Timer2 is only enabled when the control button 'circle' is clicked. The accompanying timer procedure calculates the X and Y position and directly controls the positions of the accompanying slider controls. The position control can be directly observed on the screen.

For higher demands on pulse length accuracy, when using a relatively slow computer it can be worthwhile to have the serial

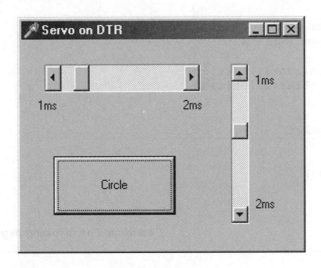

*Figure 3.5*

*Direct automatic control of two servos*

# 3 Direct Digital Outputs

*Listing 3.3* Controlling two servos connected to DTR and RTS

```
unit Servo2;

interface

uses    PORTINC, Windows, Messages, SysUtils, Classes,
  Graphics, Controls, Forms, Dialogs, ExtCtrls, StdCtrls;

type
  TForm1 = class(TForm)
    ScrollBar1: TScrollBar; Timer1: TTimer;
    Label1: TLabel; Label2: TLabel;
    ScrollBar2: TScrollBar; Label3: TLabel;
    Label4: TLabel; Button1: TButton;
    Timer2: TTimer;
    procedure Timer1Timer(Sender: TObject);
    procedure FormCreate(Sender: TObject);
    procedure Timer2Timer(Sender: TObject);
    procedure Button1Click(Sender: TObject);
  end;

var
  Form1: TForm1;
  n: Word;

implementation

{$R *.DFM}
procedure TForm1.Timer1Timer(Sender: TObject);
var PulseTime1, PulseTime2: Word;
begin
  PulseTime1 := ScrollBar1.Position;
  PulseTime2 := ScrollBar2.Position;
  RealTime (true);
  DTR (1);
  Delayus (PulseTime1);
  DTR (0);
  RTS (1);
  Delayus (PulseTime2);
  RTS (0);
  RealTime (false);
end;
```

*continued on following page . . .*

```
procedure TForm1.FormCreate(Sender: TObject);
begin
  OpenCom (Pchar('COM2:9600,N,8,1'));
  Timer1.Interval := 20;
  Timer1.Enabled := true;
  n:=0;
end;

procedure TForm1.Timer2Timer(Sender: TObject);
var Pos1, Pos2: real;
begin
  n:=n+1;
  Pos1:= (1500+ 400*sin(n/50));
  Scrollbar1.Position := Round(Pos1);
  Pos2:= (1500+ 400*cos(n/50));
  Scrollbar2.Position := Round(Pos2);
end;

procedure TForm1.Button1Click(Sender: TObject);
begin
  Timer2.Interval := 50;
  Timer2.Enabled := true;
end;

end.
```

transmitter of the COM interface, i.e. the UART TxD line, directly generate the servo pulse. At a standard communication rate of 600 baud each bit has a duration of exactly 1667 ms. When a '255' byte is sent, only the start bit appears as a single pulse, the eight following data bits being low due to the inverted signal and thus not present as pulses. The length of the pulse generated in this manner is completely PC-independent, because the UART interface chip uses its own built-in oscillator and is a pure hardware controller. In order to generate any desired pulse length, the baud rate can be set to an 'odd' value by using the Outport command to directly access the UART registers, bypassing the operating system. However, this command does not work under Windows NT.

The baud rate is controlled by a 16-bit divider factor passed to the UART, with the baud rate set to (115,200 ÷ divider). With a divider of 115, the baud rate is 1000, which corresponds to a pulse length of 1 ms, while a divider of 230 results in 500 baud and a pulse length of 2 ms. Between these limits, any one of 115 integer divider values can be used to vary the pulse length, therefore a servo can generate the same number of positions with correspondingly high precision.

Before a new baud rate can be set, the DLAB bit in the line control register must be set. Then the denominators in both baud rate registers are written, and in this case the high byte is always null. After defining the baud rate, the line control register must be refreshed with the usual data to control the other COM port settings. After that bytes can be immediately transmitted at the new baud rate. Since the operating system has been bypassed, it does not notice the change of baud rate, and it therefore treats the Sendbyte command in the usual way.

Externally, the program appears to be similar to the first program using the DTR line for control. However, it generates a much more accurate pulse on TxD. If the position of the slider control is not altered, the servo comes completely to rest in a short time.

*Figure 3.6*
*Improved*
*control program*

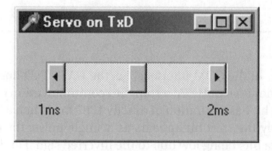

*Listing 3.4* *Using SendByte to generate more precise pulse widths*

```
unit Servo3;

interface

uses  PORTINC,Windows, Messages, SysUtils, Classes, Graphics,
      Controls, Forms, Dialogs, ExtCtrls, StdCtrls;

type
  TForm1 = class(TForm)
    ScrollBar1: TScrollBar;  Timer1: TTimer;
    Label1: TLabel;   Label2: TLabel;
    procedure Timer1Timer(Sender: TObject);
    procedure FormCreate(Sender: TObject);
  end;
var
  Form1: TForm1;

implementation

{$R *.DFM}

procedure TForm1.Timer1Timer(Sender: TObject);
var Divider : Word;
Const COM2 =$02F8;
begin
  Divider := round (0.1152 * ScrollBar1.Position);
  OutPort (COM2+3,128);      {Baudrate access}
  OutPort (COM2+0,Factor);   {Baudrate low}
  OutPort (COM2+1,0);        {Baudrate high}
  OutPort (COM2+3,3);        {8,N,1}
  SendByte (255);
end;

procedure TForm1.FormCreate(Sender: TObject);
begin
  OpenCom (Pchar('COM2:9600,N,8,1'));
  Timer1.Interval := 20;
  Timer1.Enabled := true;
end;

end.
```

## 3.3 Controlling stepping motors

A stepping motor contains a magnetic rotor and several fixed field coils. Stable positions of the rotor can be achieved by switching individual coils on and off, so the rotor can be moved stepwise. The advantage of this is that the exact position or angle of the rotor can be determined simply by counting steps, without any feedback. Standard stepping motors complete a full revolution in 100 steps (for example), so the angle can be changed in small increments. Due to the inertial mass of the rotor, stepping motors cannot be driven arbitrarily quickly. The maximum achievable speed is approximately 1000 steps per second.

Small stepping motors are usually driven unipolar, with the current through the individual windings flowing in only one direction, permitting simple control circuits to be used. The SGS ULN2803 power driver (an 8-bit, 50-V, 500-mA TTL-input Darlington NPN driver array that needs no power supply, with $V_{DD}$ connected to the common cathode of eight integrated protection diodes) provides eight open-collector transistor switch stages suitable for loads up to 500 mA. The IC also contains the necessary protection diodes for controlling inductive loads.

The controller must generate a rotating magnetic field in the motor by sequentially switching adjacent windings. If only one winding is switched at a time, the control scheme shown in the following table can be considered.

| Coil 1 | Coil 2 | Coil 3 | Coil 4 | Control value |
|--------|--------|--------|--------|---------------|
| 1 | 0 | 0 | 0 | 8 |
| 0 | 1 | 0 | 0 | 4 |
| 0 | 0 | 1 | 0 | 2 |
| 0 | 0 | 0 | 1 | 1 |
| 1 | 0 | 0 | 0 | 8 |
| 0 | 1 | 0 | 0 | 4 |
| etc. | | | | |

It is evident that four output switches are necessary. As there are only four different control values, a binary decoder can be used to produce four lines from the two DTR and RTS lines. However, there is an easier way to control a stepping motor using only two control bits, and with that two neighbouring windings always switch together, as shown in the following table.

| Coil 1 | Coil 2 | Coil 3 | Coil 4 | Control value |
|--------|--------|--------|--------|---------------|
| 1 | 1 | 0 | 0 | 3 |
| 0 | 1 | 1 | 0 | 1 |
| 0 | 0 | 1 | 1 | 0 |
| 1 | 0 | 0 | 1 | 2 |
| 1 | 1 | 0 | 0 | 3 |
| 0 | 1 | 1 | 0 | 1 |
| etc. | | | | |

With this control scheme the stepping motor requires twice as much current at the same voltage, but it also has more torque. Two-lead drive is made easier by the fact that pairs of coils are always driven opposite to each other. The control signal for coil 3 is generated by inverting the signal for coil . The same applies to coils 2 and 4. Figure 3.7 shows the motor control using a ULN2803 power driver. Since each driver stage inverts the signal, inverted signals for drivers 3 and 4 can be taken directly from the outputs for coils 1 and 2.

The states of the first two windings can be regarded as binary numbers in the sequence 3, 1, 0, 2. Controlling the motor by outputting these values to DTR and RTS must be done relatively slowly, as the highest permissible step rate of the motor is 100 to 500 steps per second, depending on the motor. It is therefore sufficient to program in Visual Basic, and the time delay can be generated with Delay or TimeRead.

A simple example program can be used to set the step position of the motor. When the Start button is pressed, the motor will

*Figure 3.7*

*2-bit control of stepping motors*

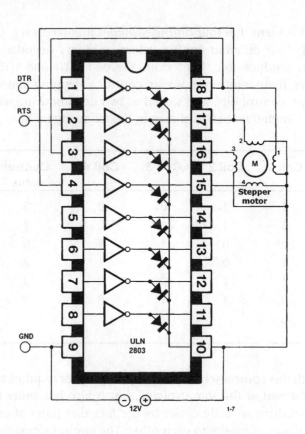

rotate the indicated number of steps. Rotation in both directions is possible. The current position of the motor rotor and the switch status are displayed in the text box. The user inputs the desired position, and the subroutine 'Output' then generates the necessary control signals on DTR and RTS until the position is reached. With appropriate mechanical construction, a linear drive can be built with many thousands of possible positions.

As in every VB project the COM port must be properly closed on program termination. This example shows a further important detail with regard to time delays. If a time delay is initiated in a procedure by using DELAY, the program appears to hang, i.e. it no longer reacts to external events, such as mouse clicks, during this time. This method can thus only be used when it completes very quickly. Longer processes, such as controlling the motion of a

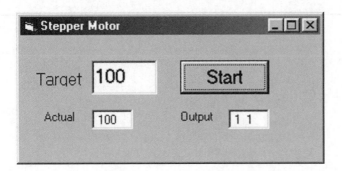

*Figure 3.8*
*Simple control*
*program*

stepping motor, should be delayed in a manner that does not stop external events from being processed. Here DELAY is not used, but instead TIMEREAD together with DoEvents. Consequently, all mouse events (for example) are handled correctly:

*Listing 3.5*
*Program for*
*2-bit stepping*
*motor control*
*(Stepper1.frm)*

```
While TIMEREAD < 10
   DoEvents
Wend
```

```
Dim Target, Actual

Private Sub Command1_Click()
   Target = Val(Text1.Text)
   Output
End Sub

Private Sub Form_Load()
   If OPENCOM("COM2:9600,N,8,1") = 0
         Then MsgBox "COM2 unavailable"
   DTR 1
   RTS 1
   Target = 0: Actual = 0
End Sub

Sub Phase1()
   DTR 1
   RTS 1
   Text3.Text = "  1    1"
End Sub
```

*continued on following page ...*

```
Sub Phase2()
   DTR 1
   RTS 0
   Text3.Text = " 1   0"
End Sub

Sub Phase3()
   DTR 0
   RTS 0
   Text3.Text = " 0   0"
End Sub

Sub Phase4()
   DTR 0
   RTS 1
   Text3.Text = " 0   1"
End Sub

Sub Output()
   While Target <> Actual
      If Target > Actual Then Actual = Actual + 1
      If Target < Actual Then Actual = Actual - 1
      Text2.Text = Str$(Actual)
      Phase = Actual Mod 4
      If Phase < 0 Then Phase = Phase + 4
      If Phase = 0 Then Phase1
      If Phase = 1 Then Phase2
      If Phase = 2 Then Phase3
      If Phase = 3 Then Phase4
      TIMEINIT
      While TIMEREAD < 10
        DoEvents
      Wend
   Wend
End Sub

Private Sub Form_Unload(Cancel As Integer)
   CLOSECOM
End Sub
```

# 4

# Direct Digital Inputs

The serial interface can read and supervise up to four logic states by direct interrogation of the handshaking lines. The input signal for different tasks can come from switches, sensors or complex amplifiers.

## 4.1 Computing transitory events

Many control processes can be represented by binary states, for example, the status of a physical door can be monitored. The door status is either 'open' or 'shut' and can be recognised by the state of, for example, burglar alarm contacts. The binary status of electronic equipment, i.e. 'on' or 'off', can be recognised by the contact status of a related relay.

In a simple serial interface configuration, four switches can be connected (see Figure 4.1 overleaf). For a long term observation it is for example meaningful that each change, of one or more event states, is stored together with an accurate time. Listing 4.1 (overleaf) shows a solution in Visual Basic, where a variable is defined for each input to store the actual state (i.e. CTS new) and one for the previous state (i.e. CTS old). Using a simple comparison it can be determined, whether a state has altered. Using this configuration a record of all events is made. On program execution all 'old' state values are initialised to –1. This means that even on the first call of the timer procedure, a change is recorded and the actual state reported.

# 4 Direct Digital Inputs

*Figure 4.1*

*Connecting four switches to the serial interface*

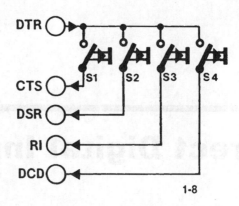

*Figure 4.2*

*Actual state report*

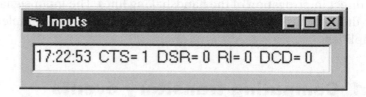

The program writes all state changes and the related timings to a text file. A text line is appended to file DATA.TXT on each change of at least one of the input switches. The output file can then be post-processed by an external program. The following table shows an example, of recorded changes to RI, CTS and DCD.

*Listing 4.1*

*Recording switch events*

```
Dim CTSnew, DSRnew, RInew, DCDnew
Dim CTSold, DSRold, RIold, DCDold

Private Sub Form_Load()
    If OPENCOM("COM2:9600,N,8,1") = 0
        Then MsgBox "COM2 unavailable"
    DTR 1
    CTSold = -1: DSRold = -1: RIold = -1: DCDold = -1
End Sub
```

***continued on following page ...***

```
Private Sub Form_Unload(Cancel As Integer)
  CLOSECOM
End Sub

Private Sub Timer1_Timer()
  CTSnew = CTS: DSRnew = DSR: RInew = RI: DCDnew = DCD
  If (CTSnew <> CTSold) Or (DSRnew <> DSRold) Or
    (RInew <> RIold) Or (DCDnew <> DCDold) Then Output
  CTSold = CTSnew: DSRold = DSRnew
  RIold = RInew: DCDold = DCDnew
End Sub

Sub Output()
  Status$ = Time$ + "   CTS=" + Str$(CTSnew) + "   DSR="
       + Str$(DSRnew) + "   RI=" + Str$(RInew) + "   DCD="
       + Str$(DCDnew)
  Text1.Text = Status$
  Open "Data.TXT" For Append As #1
  Print #1, Status$
  Close 1
End Sub
```

```
09:47:19    CTS=0 DSR=0 RI=0   DCD=0
09:47:26    CTS=0 DSR=0 RI=1   DCD=0
09:47:31    CTS=0 DSR=0 RI=0   DCD=0
09:47:33    CTS=1 DSR=0 RI=0   DCD=0
09:47:36    CTS=0 DSR=0 RI=0   DCD=0
09:47:48    CTS=0 DSR=0 RI=0   DCD=1
09:47:50    CTS=0 DSR=0 RI=0   DCD=0
```

Instead of switches, other devices can be used, for example, a photoresistor or other input device. A practical application is recording of electrical consumption versus time, and the Computer can help here with the planning of energy economy measures.

## 4.2 Simulating logic circuits

Digital circuits process input values to output values using logic rules. The normal Boolean functions are the AND, NAND, OR, NOR and the XOR functions. Most high-level languages provide these functions, permitting easier program writing for modelling digital circuit behaviour. For practical purposes, such programs are also suitable for logical control of equipment.

The following is the truth table for logical Boolean functions with inputs A and B:

| A | B | Output: | AND | NAND | OR | NOR | XOR |
|---|---|---------|-----|------|----|----|-----|
| 0 | 0 |         | 0   | 1    | 0  | 1  | 0   |
| 0 | 1 |         | 0   | 1    | 1  | 0  | 1   |
| 1 | 0 |         | 0   | 1    | 1  | 0  | 1   |
| 1 | 1 |         | 1   | 0    | 1  | 0  | 0   |

For the experiment two input switches per single output element are needed, with an LED providing the result. Figure 4.3 shows the circuitry connected to the interface, and Listing 4.2 shows a program solution in Visual Basic. The user can select the required logical functions with the radio buttons. Both the input and output states are shown in the program window.

*Figure 4.3*

*Simulation of Boolean logic with two inputs and one output*

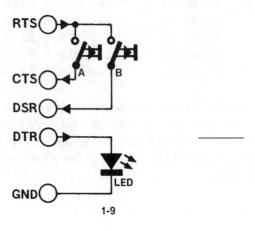

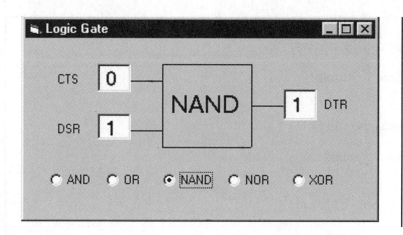

*Figure 4.4*
*Logic.frm*
*program*
*window*

*Listing 4.2*
*Logical*
*coupling of*
*input states*

```
Dim Logic

Private Sub Form_Load()
    If OPENCOM("COM2:9600,N,8,1") = 0 Then MsgBox "COM2
        unavailable"
    RTS 1
    Logic = 1
End Sub

Private Sub Form_Unload(Cancel As Integer)
    CLOSECOM
End Sub

Private Sub Option1_Click()
    Logic = 1
    Label3.Caption = "AND"
End Sub

Private Sub Option2_Click()
    Logic = 2
    Label3.Caption = "OR"
End Sub
```

*continued on following page . . .*

```
Private Sub Option3_Click()
   Logic = 3
   Label3.Caption = "NAND"
End Sub

Private Sub Option4_Click()
   Logic = 4
   Label3.Caption = "NOR"
End Sub

Private Sub Option5_Click()
   Logic = 5
   Label3.Caption = "XOR"
End Sub

Private Sub Timer1_Timer()
   A = CTS: B = DSR
   Text1.Text = Str$(A)
   Text2.Text = Str$(B)
   If Logic = 1 Then C = A And B
   If Logic = 2 Then C = A Or B
   If Logic = 3 Then C = (Not (A And B)) And 1
   If Logic = 4 Then C = (Not (A Or B)) And 1
   If Logic = 5 Then C = A Xor B
   Text3.Text = Str$(C)
   DTR C
End Sub
```

# Simple Analogue/Digital Converters

An analogue to digital converter transforms an analogue signal such as a voltage, resistance, or a temperature, into a numerical value, which can then be computer processed. To ensure the numerical value is accurately defined, the analogue signal must be divided into discrete ranges, the greatest width of which is dependent on the converter resolution. For example, with a voltage resolution of 100 mV, all voltages between 1.10 V and 1.19 V are measured with 0.1 V accuracy.

With few additional semiconductors, analogue values can be transformed into discrete length pulses, which can be directly Computer measured. The following applications demonstrate lowest cost circuits for analogue inputs.

## 5.1 Resistance measurement

A simple RC network generates a time delay, which is proportional to the resistance and capacitance. For example, a DTR pulse can be generated, and the pulse delay measured on a digital input. The time delay is a measure of the analogue quantity being measured. Since all RS232 inputs possess Schmitt triggers, a well defined switching signal can be generated even with slowly rising input voltages.

# 5 Simple Analogue/Digital Converters

Figure 5.1 shows a potentiometer polling circuit, with each pot position being assigned a numerical value. The polling program requires a fast counting loop as the measured time delay lies in the millisecond range. Listing 5.1 shows a solution in Delphi, in which the virtual time measurement uses 'TimeReadus' in microseconds.

Using values of 1 μF and 10 kΩ, a charging time of circa 4.5 ms results. With R = 0 approximately 1 ms is measured, because the DTR output provides a maximum load current of approximately 10mA to the capacitor. The whole measuring range extends to circa 3.5ms with a theoretical resolution of 1μs. This actually achieves a resolution which is highly dependent on the utilised PC, and for a Pentium 200 is about 5 μs. The call to RealTime(true) increases measurement reliability by setting other concurrent processes to a lower priority.

The measurement loop polls the CTS line until a '1' state is detected. At the same time, a timeout limit of 10,000 μs is set, in case of an error. The complete measurement needs a discrete recovery time for capacitor discharge. With a Timer value of 1000 ms, adequate discharge time is guaranteed with a repetition rate of one measurement per second.

**Figure 5.1**

*Resistance measurement by means of charging time*

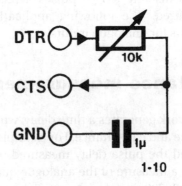

DTR

10k

CTS

GND

1μ

1-10

It is not only potentiometers which can be used by this measuring equipment, as many sensors work according to the principle of resistance change. Examples are NTC's for temperature measurement and LDR's for sampling light intensity. Non-electrical values such as temperature and light can therefore be determined via the measured pulse length.

*Listing 5.1*
*Simple*
*polling loop*
*for resistance*
*measurement*

```
unit AD1;

interface

uses
   PORTINC, Windows, Messages, SysUtils, Classes, Graphics,
   Controls, Forms, Dialogs, StdCtrls, ComCtrls, ExtCtrls;

type
   TForm1 = class(TForm)
      Timer1: TTimer;   Edit1: TEdit;
      procedure FormCreate(Sender: TObject);
      procedure Timer1Timer(Sender: TObject);
end;

var
   Form1: TForm1;

implementation

{$R *.DFM}
```

**continued on following page ...**

# 5 Simple Analogue/Digital Converters

```
procedure TForm1.FormCreate(Sender: TObject);
begin
  OpenCom(pchar('com2:9600,N,8,1'));
  DTR(0);
end;

procedure TForm1.Timer1Timer(Sender: TObject);
var Output:String;
    Time: DWord;
begin
  RealTime (true);
  DTR (1);
  TimeInitus;
  While((CTS=0) and (TimeReadus < 10000)) do;
  Time:=TimeReadus;
  DTR (0);
  Str(Time,Output);
  Edit1.Text := Output + ' us';
  RealTime (false);
end;

end.
```

## 5.2 Voltage measurement

For voltage measurement, only an RC network and an operational amplifier are required, the latter being used as a comparator. Figure 5.3 shows a circuit with a single input channel. The operational amplifier needs circa –10 V and +10 V direct from the interface. There is adequate space in a sub-D type connector shell for these components.

The circuit function is easy to understand: when DTR switches high, the capacitor begins to charge, and its voltage is continuously compared to the input voltage. As soon as the input voltage is reached, the output of the operational amplifier changes state. The higher the voltage measurement is, the later this transition

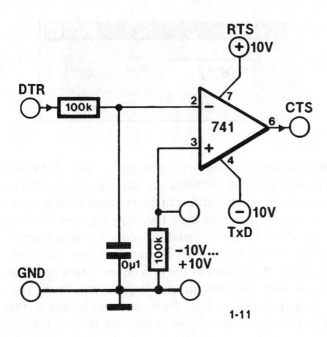

*Figure 5.3*

*A/D converter
using the pulse
width method*

occurs, therefore measuring the time delay enables the input volt-age to be determined. If the input voltage is zero, the charging time with the indicated component values is approximately 8 ms.

Unfortunately, the capacitor voltage rise is non-linear, being determined directly by the voltage drop over the charging resis-tance. With increasing capacitor charge and increasing voltage, the voltage across the capacitor rises more slowly. It thus follows an exponential curve.Using electronic circuitry alone it is very dif-ficult to linearise this function, however a linearisation in the pro-gram is relatively simple. A concise mathematical correlation can be programmed between the measurement time and correspond-ing voltage.

Listing 5.2 (overleaf) shows the measurement program, the measurement again being based on a numerical count. The dif-ference with Listing 5.1 is that a function is used instead of a pro-cedure. The numerical result must then be further processed to calculate the voltage. As well as the DTR line, the RTS line must also be permanently switched high, so that the positive working voltage of the operational amplifiers is available over this line.

# 5  Simple Analogue/Digital Converters

**Figure 5.4**

*Voltage measurement in Delphi*

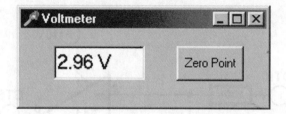

The function 'Counter' returns the length of the charging pulse in microseconds. Fortunately, the measured value is computer-independent, in contrast to the measurement accuracy. The input voltage is calculated from the charging time, which is related to the the R–C time constant. Accurate measurement of the time constant is not necessary if automatic zero point measurement is used. This occurs in the procedure 'Calibrate', where the zero-point value for zero input voltage is measured. When the program is started, therefore, there must not be any voltage present, i.e. the input may be open or shorted. With all the following measurements, the measured voltage is given in proportion to the actual counter value and zero point value.

The counter value formula for voltage measurements is derived using the exponential curve of the loaded capacitor. It states that the rate of voltage increase of a capacitor loaded over a resistance, decreases the closer the capacitor voltage and load voltage become. The exponential function describes this continuously flattening voltage slope, and the measurement linearisation is defined in accordance with the formula:

Voltage = 20V * (1 – exp(–Counter/Zero point)) – 10V

When measuring equipment is tested in both polarities, i.e. first positive then negative, for example with a battery, then a slight non-linearity will be found. The presupposition, that the DTR output voltage becomes –10 V and +10 V, is not perfectly accurate. By changing the constant values of 'negative' and 'positive', the linearisation can be substantially improved. With careful adjustment an overall accuracy of about one percent can be achieved.

A/D converter resolution depends therefore, on how accurately the computer can measure the time delay of R–C networks. Accordingly, a faster computer produces a significantly more accurate result. With the depicted circuit and a Pentium-200 the resolution correlates approximately to a 10-bit A/D converter. The related voltage resolution becomes 10 mV, so it can sample up to 2000 different voltages values, thereby approaching the quality of simple digital voltmeters.

One disadvantage of this procedure lies in its relatively slow response. In order to achieve a comparison voltage close to the lower end of the measuring range at the start of each new conversion, a time delay of more than 0.1 s between two measurements must be used.

*Listing 5.2*
*Delphi program for a simple digital voltmeter*

```
unit ADU1;

interface

uses
PORTINC, Windows, Messages, SysUtils, Classes, Graphics,
Controls, Forms, Dialogs, StdCtrls, ComCtrls, ExtCtrls;

type
  TForm1 = class(TForm)
    Timer1: TTimer;    Edit1: TEdit;
    Button1: TButton;
    procedure FormCreate(Sender: TObject);
    procedure Timer1Timer(Sender: TObject);
    procedure Button1Click(Sender: TObject);
  end;

var
  Form1: TForm1;
  Zerop: Real;
const Neg = 10.2;
      Pos = 10.25;
```

***continued on following page ...***

```
implementation

{$R *.DFM}

function Counter: Double;
var  Time : Double;
begin
  RealTime (true);
  DTR (1);
  TimeInitus;
  While(( CTS=1) and (TimeReadus < 50000)) do;
  Time:=TimeReadus;
  DTR (0);
  RealTime (false);
  Counter := Time;
end;

procedure Zeropoint;
begin
  delay (500);
  Zerop := -(Counter/ln(1-Neg/(Pos+Neg)));
  Delay (500);
end;

procedure TForm1.FormCreate(Sender: TObject);
begin
  OpenCom(pchar('com2:9600,N,8,1'));
  DTR(0);
  RTS (1);
  TXD (0);
  Timer1.Enabled := false;
  delay (500);
  Zerop := -(Counter/ln(1-Neg/(Pos+Neg)));
  Delay (500);
  Timer1.Enabled := false;
  Zeropoint;
  Timer1.Enabled := true;
end;
```

*continued on following page . . .*

```
procedure TForm1.Timer1Timer(Sender: TObject);
var Output:String;
    Time: Double;
    Voltage:Real;
begin
  Time := Counter;
  Voltage := (neg+Pos)*(1-exp(-Time/Zerop))-Neg;
  Voltage := round(Voltage*100)/100;
  Edit1.Text := floattostr(Voltage) + ' V';
end;

procedure TForm1.Button1Click(Sender: TObject);
begin
  Timer1.Enabled := false;
  Zeropoint;
  Timer1.Enabled := true;
end;

end.
```

## 5.3 Four-channel A/D converter

A review of the serial interface input port shows that up to four analogue input channels are possible, and four comparators can share the same RC-combination. With this expansion a weakness of the basic A/D circuit can be overcome. The timing measurement accuracy depends on the Computers output voltage, i.e. it depends on the power supply and on the serial interface line drivers. To obtain a better reference voltage accuracy, as in Figure 5.5, two stabilising Zener diodes are used. With that the measurement range is narrowed to approximately –8 V to +8 V.

In addition, the operational amplifiers voltage supply is freed from transient impulse disturbance by blocking capacitors. Inputs 1 and 2 are provided with a 100-kΩ input resistor so the input voltage in the idle state is zero. Both other input channels are used without input resistors, leaving them at a very high impedance, so that even very high resistance measuring objects can be used without any voltage drop.However, this does not permit working with open input channels, which could lead to input voltages outside the measurement range.

The quadruple operational amplifier LM324 needs only 1 mA and can manage the interface problem free. As there is no requirement for a battery or external PSU, the four channel version of the A/D converter requires few skills to install in a connector shell.

**Figure 5.5**

*Simple 4-channel A/D converter without additional power supply*

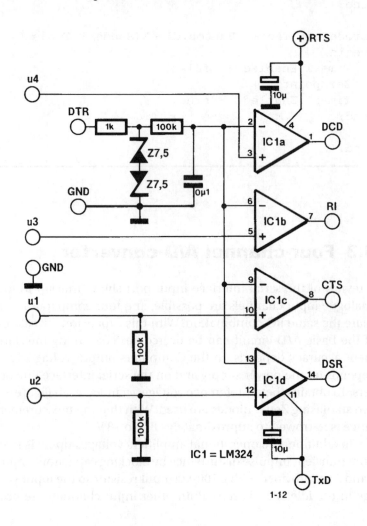

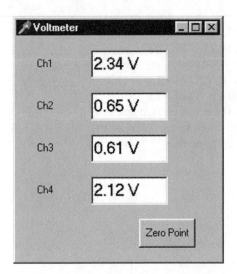

*Figure 5.6*
*Four-channel*
*measurement*
*equipment*
*window*

The program in Listing 5.3 uses a redesigned 'Counter' function, which this time is called with the desired input channel. With each measurement only one input line is observed, while on reading the port address the bit with a decimal value of 16, 32, 64 or 128 is evaluated. In addition, measurement linearisation is this time provided by a function. The function 'Voltage' provides the measurement result directly on a given input channel.

In the main program the channel 1 to 4 voltages are subsequently displayed, making four independent digital volt meters available.

*Listing 5.3*
*Multi-channel*
*digital voltmeter*
*program*

```
unit ADU4;

interface

uses
   PORTINC, Windows, Messages, SysUtils, Classes, Graphics,
   Controls, Forms, Dialogs, StdCtrls, ComCtrls, ExtCtrls;

type
   TForm1 = class(TForm)
```
***continued on following page ...***

```
      Timer1: TTimer; Edit1: TEdit;
      Button1: TButton; Edit2: TEdit;
      Edit3: TEdit; Edit4: TEdit;
      Label1: TLabel; Label2: TLabel;
      Label3: TLabel; Label4: TLabel;
      procedure FormCreate(Sender: TObject);
      procedure Timer1Timer(Sender: TObject);
      procedure Button1Click(Sender: TObject);
end;

var
   Form1: TForm1;
   Zerop: Real;
const Neg = 8.2;
       Pos = 8.2;

implementation

{$R *.DFM}

function Counter (Channel: Integer): Double;
begin
   RealTime (true);
   DTR (1);
   TimeInitus;
   Case Channel of
   1:    While(( CTS=1) and (TimeReadus < 50000)) do;
   2:    While(( DSR=1) and (TimeReadus < 50000)) do;
   3:    While(( RI=1) and (TimeReadus < 50000)) do;
   4:    While(( DCD=1) and (TimeReadus < 50000)) do;
   end;
   Counter := TimeReadus;
   DTR (0);
   RealTime (false);
end;

procedure Zeropoint;
begin
   delay (500);
```

*continued on following page . . .*

```
  Zerop := -(Counter(1)/ln(1-Neg/(Pos+Neg)));
  Delay (500);
end;

procedure TForm1.FormCreate(Sender: TObject);
begin
  OpenCom(pchar('com2:9600,N,8,1'));
  DTR(0);
  RTS (1);
  TXD (0);
  Timer1.Enabled := false;
  Zeropoint;
  Timer1.Enabled := true;
end;

function Voltage(Channel:Integer):Real;
var u:Real;
begin
  U := (neg+Pos)*(1-exp(-Counter(Channel)/Zerop))-Neg;
  Voltage := Round(U*100)/100;
  delay (150);
end;

procedure TForm1.Timer1Timer(Sender: TObject);
begin
  Edit1.Text := floattostr(Voltage(1)) + ' V';
  Edit2.Text := floattostr(Voltage(2)) + ' V';
  Edit3.Text := floattostr(Voltage(3)) + ' V';
  Edit4.Text := floattostr(Voltage(4)) + ' V';
end;

procedure TForm1.Button1Click(Sender: TObject);
begin
  Timer1.Enabled := false;
  Zeropoint;
  Timer1.Enabled := true;
end;

end.
```

## 5.4 Transistor measurements

As well as digital multimeters, the four-channel A/D converter can be used for many other multi-facetted applications, thereby exceeding the capabilities of common measuring equipment. Particularly interesting is automatic measurement, where multiple calculations are executed concurrently. A simple example for the possible use of equipment is transistor circuit analysis. The input voltage can be set by a potentiometer and with that the base current varied. The measuring equipment catches numerous values which are dependent on the base current. Figure 5.7 shows the measurement structure and the connection of the measurement inputs. All voltages are measured from a common ground.

*Figure 5.7*

*Investigation of an NPN transistor in common-emitter configuration*

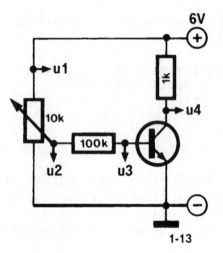

The possibility exists under Windows, to model this measurement structure. Actual measured values can be displayed in the circuit diagram, thereby presenting measurements with greater clarity. The program is very useful for educational purposes, and for testing transistor parameters.

In the given circuit, not only voltages, but also the base and the collector currents are measurable. Using both values, the transistors current amplification, i.e. the gain factor h$fe$ can be deter-

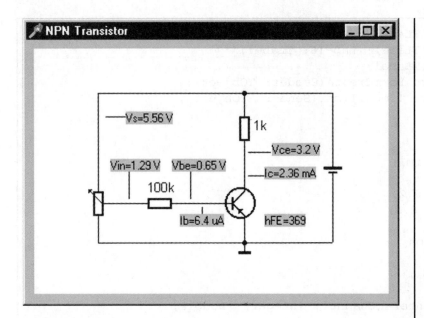

**NPN Transistor**

Vs=5.56 V
1k
Vce=3.2 V
Vin=1.29 V   Vbe=0.65 V
Ic=2.36 mA
100k
Ib=6.4 uA
hFE=369

*Figure 5.8*
*Virtual
measurement
circuit
modelling
physical
measuring
equipment*

mined. The current amplification is calculated using both the voltage drop over the base resistor and the collector resistor. Both voltage drops are the difference between directly measurable voltages. Listing 5.4 shows a program, where all important measured values inclusive of the current amplification are calculated.

*Listing 5.4
Program to
measure hfe
at various
operating
points*

```
unit NPN;

interface

uses
   PORTINC, Windows, Messages, SysUtils, Classes, Graphics,
   Controls, Forms, Dialogs, StdCtrls, ComCtrls, ExtCtrls;

type
   TForm1 = class(TForm)
      Timer1: TTimer; Image1: TImage;
      Label1: TLabel; Label2: TLabel;
```

*continued on following page . . .*

```
      Label3: TLabel; Label4: TLabel;
      Label5: TLabel; Label6: TLabel;
      Label7: TLabel;
      procedure FormCreate(Sender: TObject);
      procedure Timer1Timer(Sender: TObject);
   end;

var
   Form1: TForm1;
   Zerop: Real;
const Neg = 8.2;
      Pos = 8.2;

implementation

{$R *.DFM}

function Counter (Channel: Integer): Double;
begin
   RealTime (true);
   DTR (1);
   TimeInitus;
   Case Channel of
   1:    While(( CTS=1) and (TimeReadus < 50000)) do;
   2:    While(( DSR=1) and (TimeReadus < 50000)) do;
   3:    While(( RI=1) and (TimeReadus < 50000)) do;
   4:    While(( DCD=1) and (TimeReadus < 50000)) do;
   end;
   Counter := TimeReadus;
   DTR (0);
   RealTime (false);
end;

procedure Zeropoint;
begin
   delay (500);
   Zerop := -(Counter(1)/ln(1-Neg/(Pos+Neg)));
   Delay (500);
end;
```

*continued on following page . . .*

```
procedure TForm1.FormCreate(Sender: TObject);
begin
  OpenCom(pchar('com2:9600,N,8,1'));
  DTR(0);
  RTS (1);
  TXD (0);
  Timer1.Enabled := false;
  Zeropoint;
  Timer1.Enabled := true;
end;

function Voltage(Channel:Integer):Real;
var u:Real;
begin
  U := (neg+Pos)*(1-exp(-Counter(Channel)/Zerop))-Neg;
  Voltage := Round(U*100)/100;
  delay (150);
end;

procedure TForm1.Timer1Timer(Sender: TObject);
var U1,U2,U3,U4,Ib,Ic,V: Real;
begin
  U1:=Voltage(1); U2:=Voltage(2);
  U3:=Voltage(3); U4:=Voltage(4);
  Ib:=(U2-U3)*10;
  Ic:=U1-U4;
  V:=Round(Ic/(Ib+0.00001)*1000);
  Ib:= round(Ib*100)/100;
  Ic:= round(Ic*100)/100;
  Label1.Caption := 'Ub='+floattostr(U1) + ' V';
  Label2.Caption := 'Uin='+floattostr(U2) + ' V';
  Label3.Caption := 'Ube='+floattostr(U3) + ' V';
  Label4.Caption := 'Uce='+floattostr(U4) + ' V';
  Label5.Caption := 'Ib='+floattostr(Ib) + ' uA';
  Label6.Caption := 'Ic='+floattostr(Ic) + ' mA';
  Label7.Caption := 'V='+floattostr(V);
end;

end.
```

# 6

# Frequency Measurements

For frequency measurement, both a suitable counter and an accurate time base are needed. The frequency in Hertz can be obtained by counting all pulses arriving within an accurately measured period of one second. Usually digital meters process frequencies in the megahertz range. For many jobs however, PC frequency measurement can be sufficient up to a few kilohertz, and in these cases the PC can replace a digital meter.

## 6.1 Software counter

When the input channels of the serial interface are used, then input signals between approximately 2 V and 12 V can be completely processed without additional electronics. As there are four directly readable input channels, four measurement channels can be realised (see Figure 6.1). Listing 6.1 shows an appropriate

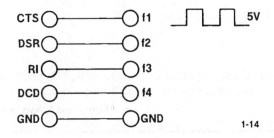

*Figure 6.1*

*Four inputs for frequency measurement*

# 6 Frequency Measurements

**Figure 6.2**

*Displaying up to four frequencies*

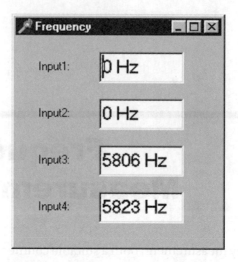

Delphi program for frequency measurement on four channels. Using this program, a Pentium 200 can achieve an upper limit frequency of approximately 10 kHz.

The program uses the DLL function 'TimeReadus' as a time base. The procedure 'Frequency' counts all positive edges of the respective inputs during a one second interval. At any discrete time the actual status of the input channel is compared with that last observed. To improve reliable identification of all input pulses, the 'Realtime(true)' procedure is called. Nevertheless in the upper frequency range, increased measurement errors may occur when the system drops pulses during other tasks. It is thus necessary to measure the upper frequency limit using the allocated PC before making practical measurements.

**Listing 6.1**

*Quadruple frequency measurement program*

```
unit Freq4;

interface

uses
   PORTINC, Windows, Messages, SysUtils, Classes, Graphics,
   Controls, Forms, Dialogs, StdCtrls, ComCtrls, ExtCtrls;
```
***continued on following page ...***

```
type
  TForm1 = class(TForm)
    Timer1: TTimer; Edit1: TEdit;
    Edit2: TEdit; Edit3: TEdit;
    Edit4: TEdit; Label1: TLabel;
    Label2: TLabel; Label3: TLabel;
    Label4: TLabel;
    procedure FormCreate(Sender: TObject);
    procedure Timer1Timer(Sender: TObject);
end;

var
  Form1: TForm1;

implementation

{$R *.DFM}

function Frequency (Channel: Integer): Integer;
var Counter, old, Input : Integer;
begin
  Counter := 0;
  RealTime (true);
  TimeInitus;
  Case Channel of
  1:    begin
          old:=CTS;
          while TimeReadus < 1000000 do begin
            Input := CTS;
            if Input> old then Counter := Counter +1;
            Old := Input;
          end;
        end;
  2:    begin
          old:=DSR;
          while TimeReadus < 1000000 do begin
            Input := DSR;
            if Input> old then Counter := Counter +1;
            Old:= Input;
          end;
        end;
```

*continued on following page ...*

```
   3:      begin
             old:=RI;
             while TimeReadus < 1000000 do begin
               Input  := RI;
               if Input> old then Counter := Counter +1;
               Old:= Input;
             end;
           end;
   4:      begin
             old:=DCD;
             while TimeReadus < 1000000 do begin
               Input  := DCD;
               if Input> old then Counter := Counter +1;
               Old := Input;
             end;
           end;
   end;
   Frequency := Counter;
   RealTime (false);
end;

procedure TForm1.FormCreate(Sender: TObject);
begin
   OpenCom(pchar('com2:9600,N,8,1'));
   Timer1.Interval := 5000;
   Timer1.Enabled := true;
end;

procedure TForm1.Timer1Timer(Sender: TObject);
begin
   Edit1.Text := floattostr(Frequency(1)) + ' Hz';
   Edit2.Text := floattostr(Frequency(2)) + ' Hz';
   Edit3.Text := floattostr(Frequency(3)) + ' Hz';
   Edit4.Text := floattostr(Frequency(4)) + ' Hz';
end;

end.
```

## 6.2 Measuring air temperature and humidity

Air temperature and humidity are important parameters for judging both room climate and weather observations. PC data acquisition can be helpful for long term observation, planning or automatic control. A simple cable connection can be considered for such measurements, which are often remote from the PC site. This method of frequency measurement permits problem-free connection with two-core cables over a distance of around 30 m.

A further advantage of frequency measurement is the very fine resolution using simple devices and equipment. Figure 6.3 shows oscillators with the CMOS timer TLC555, that will be tuned by the influence of the sensors. Connections CTS and DSR serve as input channels, leaving two inputs free for expansion.

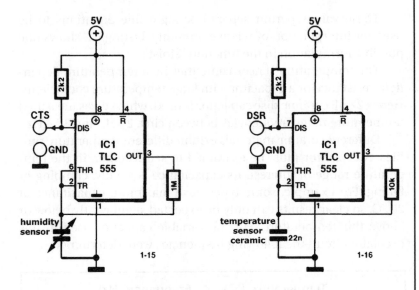

*Figure 6.3*

*Capacitance to frequency converter for measuring temperature and humidity*

The Philips humidity sensor is a capacitor with a special dielectric whose capacitance increases with increasing relative humidity. Using this sensor an oscillator can be built for a frequency range of 5 kHz, the frequency then being dependent on the relative humidity. The inter-dependency of humidity and capacitance is non linear, so the evaluation program must carry out an appropriate linearisation.

For linearisation, measured values between known points are interpolated. During frequency measurement with a known humidity the following definitive points were determined:

| Relative humidity (%) | Frequency (Hz) |
|:---:|:---:|
| 100 | 4520 |
| 80 | 4897 |
| 60 | 5262 |
| 40 | 5509 |
| 20 | 5828 |
| 0 | 6027 |

These values permit separate straight line equations to be used for interpolation of relative humidity. Listing 6.2 shows one possible formulation in the function 'Moist'.

The temperature sensor can either be a temperature dependent resistance or a capacitor with large temperature coefficients. Here a 22 nF ceramic disc capacitor is used, which gives measured temperature range frequencies between circa 2 kHz and 3.5 kHz.

Different ceramic materials exhibit different temperature profiles. A capacitor must be examined to see whether, in the temperature range of interest, its capacitance is steady, climbing or falling. For example, some types have maximum capacitance at 20 °C, so clear results can only be expected significantly below or above this temperature. For the variable capacitor used in this oscillator circuit the following frequencies were determined:

| Temperature (°C) | Frequency (Hz) |
|:---:|:---:|
| 0 | 2065 |
| 10 | 2223 |
| 20 | 2475 |
| 30 | 2835 |
| 40 | 3430 |

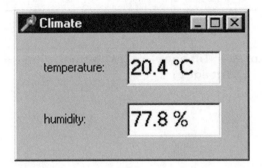

***Figure 6.4***
*Display of climate measurements*

The above points are used in the function 'Temperature' for interpolated computation of temperature. The program shows the temperature and the co-existent relative humidity. It can be simply expanded to four measurement channels, making it useful for both inside and outside measurements.

***Listing 6.2***
*Temperature and relative humidity measurement versus frequency change*

```
unit Temp1u;

interface

uses
   PORTINC, Windows, Messages, SysUtils, Classes, Graphics,
   Controls, Forms, Dialogs, StdCtrls, ComCtrls, ExtCtrls;

type
   TForm1 = class(TForm)
      Timer1: TTimer; Edit1: TEdit;
      Edit2: TEdit; Label1: TLabel;
      Label2: TLabel;
      procedure FormCreate(Sender: TObject);
      procedure Timer1Timer(Sender: TObject);
end;

var
   Form1: TForm1;

implementation
```
***continued on following page . . .***

# 6 Frequency Measurements

```
{$R *.DFM}

function Frequency (Channel: Integer): Integer;
var Counter, old, Input : Integer;
begin
  Counter := 0;
  RealTime (true);
  TimeInitus;
  Case Channel of
  1:    begin
          old:=CTS;
          while TimeReadus < 1000000 do begin
            Input := CTS;
            if Input> old then Counter := Counter +1;
            Old := Input;
          end;
        end;
  2:    begin
          old:=DSR;
          while TimeReadus < 1000000 do begin
            Input := DSR;
            if Input> old then Counter := Counter +1;
            Old := Input;
          end;
        end;
  3:    begin
          old:=RI;
          while TimeReadus < 1000000 do begin
            Input := RI;
            if Input> old then Counter := Counter +1;
            Old := Input;
          end;
        end;
  4:    begin
          old:=DCD;
          while TimeReadus < 1000000 do begin
            Input := DCD;
            if Input> old then Counter := Counter +1;
            Old := Input;
```

*continued on following page ...*

```
        end;
      end;
  end;
  Frequency := Counter;
  RealTime (false);
end;

function Moist: Real;
var MeasureFreq: Integer;
begin
  Moist := 0;
  MeasureFreq := Frequency(1);
  if MeasureFreq > 4520 then
     Moist := 100 - 20 * (MeasureFreq-4520) / (4897-4520);
  if MeasureFreq > 4897 then
     Moist := 80 - 20 * (MeasureFreq-4897) / (5262-4897);
  if MeasureFreq > 5262 then
     Moist := 60 - 20 * (MeasureFreq-5262) / (5509-5262);
  if MeasureFreq > 5509 then
     Moist := 40 - 20 * (MeasureFreq-5509) / (5828-5509);
  if MeasureFreq > 5828 then
     Moist := 20 - 20 * (MeasureFreq-5828) / (6027-5828);
end;

function Temperature: Real;
var MeasureFreq : Integer;
begin
  MeasureFreq := Frequency(2);
  Temperature := 10 * (MeasureFreq-2065) / (2230-2065);   if
     MeasureFreq > 2230 then
     Temperature := 10 + 10 * (MeasureFreq-2230) / (2475-
     2230);
  if MeasureFreq > 2475 then
     Temperature := 20 + 10 * (MeasureFreq-2475) / (2835-
     2475);
  if MeasureFreq > 2835 then
     Temperature := 30 + 10 * (MeasureFreq-2835) / (3430-
     2835);
end;
```

*continued on following page ...*

```
procedure TForm1.FormCreate(Sender: TObject);
begin
   OpenCom(pchar('com2:9600,N,8,1'));
   Timer1.Interval := 3000;
   Timer1.Enabled := true;
end;

procedure TForm1.Timer1Timer(Sender: TObject);
begin
   Edit1.Text := FloatToStrF(Temperature,ffGeneral,3,4) + '
      °C';
   Edit2.Text := FloatToStrF(Moist,ffGeneral,3,4) + ' %';
end;

end.
```

## 6.3 Voltage / frequency converter

Direct frequency measurement with the PC guarantees in principle a very fine timing accuracy and resolution. Similar acceptable results can be achieved for other measurement parameters, when they can be converted into frequencies. The voltage/frequency converter (V/f converter) AD654 from Analogue Devices converts a voltage in range of 0–1 V into a frequency with very fine linearity. Its output signal can be evaluated directly over the serial interface.

Figure 6.5 shows the V/f converter circuit. Pin 1 of the AD654 generates a symmetrical rectangular signal, its frequency being proportional to the input voltage. As the output is an open collector, a pull up resistance must be applied. With the circuit shown, a voltage of 1 V corresponds to a frequency of 10 kHz. The 10-nF capacitor can be changed, to fit with the frequency range of other output signals. For example with a 1-nF capacitor a voltage of 1V corresponds to a frequency of 100 kHz. A high-value foil capacitor must be used, which is stable at the required temperature. An accurate frequency adjustment or calibration is possible, when the 1-kΩ resistance is replaced by a trimming potentiometer. The input voltage in the range 0–1 V should not be exceeded, and for over voltage protection a resistance of 10 kΩ is inserted.

While normal A/D converters have a limited resolution, the resolution of a V/f converter is primarily dependent on the frequency measurement. The frequency measurement method shown in listing 6.1 delivers a resolution of 10 thousand steps in a range of 10 kHz with a one second measurement period. The voltage also resolves into steps of 0.1 mV. With a longer gate time the resolution increases further, so that for example 0.01 mV can be achieved.

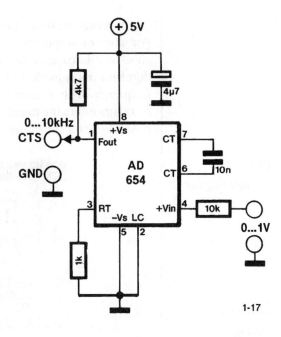

*Figure 6.5*

*Voltage to frequency converter using the AD654*

Listing 6.3 introduces a measurement program with acceptable resolution. Compared to Listing 6.1 the measurement function 'Frequency' receives the gate time in milliseconds as a handover parameter. For example, if a value of 10,000 is passed in, the measurement lasts 10 seconds. To calculate the frequency, pulses counted during this period are divided by ten, therefore the function 'Frequency' is declared as a Real value.

The Delphi program U.F.EXE permits the required resolution to be selected by corresponding buttons. According to the resolution value, it changes, the gate time of frequency measurement; the repetition time of a timer used to automatically repeat the measurement; and the output format. The voltage is output corresponding to the defined resolution with zero, one or two decimal places. The voltage calculation in millivolts requires in essence a division by ten. Additionally, a software calibration with the factor 'Calibration' is offered. Instead of a hardware calibration by adjustment of the 1-kΩ resistances, this factor can be adjusted by means comparative measurements.

# 6 Frequency Measurements

A Pentium 200 can certainly measure a frequency of 10 kHz. For slower computers is it necessary to work with lower frequencies. In this case, it can be necessary to increase the frequency determining capacitor of the AD654 and compensate for the lower frequency, with a greater measurement time. Conversely for very fast computers the measurement frequency can be raised, making possible faster measurement with higher resolution.

*Figure 6.6*
*Voltage display*

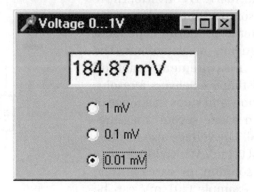

*Listing 6.3*

*Voltage Measurement with a V/f converter*

```
unit UF;

interface

uses
   PORTINC, Windows, Messages, SysUtils, Classes, Graphics,
   Controls, Forms, Dialogs, StdCtrls, ComCtrls, ExtCtrls;

type
   TForm1 = class(TForm)
     Timer1: TTimer; Edit1: TEdit;
     RadioButton1: TRadioButton;
     RadioButton2: TRadioButton;
     RadioButton3: TRadioButton;
```
*continued on following page . . .*

```
    procedure FormCreate(Sender: TObject);
    procedure Timer1Timer(Sender: TObject);
    procedure RadioButton1Click(Sender: TObject);
    procedure RadioButton2Click(Sender: TObject);
    procedure RadioButton3Click(Sender: TObject);
end;

var
  Form1: TForm1;
  Resolution: Integer;
const Calibration = 1.0000;

implementation

{$R *.DFM}

function Frequency (Gatetime: Integer): Real;
var Counter, old, Input : Integer;
begin
  Counter := 0;
  RealTime (true);
  TimeInitus;
  old:=CTS;
  while TimeReadus < (1000*Gatetime) do begin
    Input := CTS;
    if Input> old then Counter := Counter +1;
    Old := Input;
  end;
  Frequency := Counter/Gatetime*1000;
  RealTime (false);
end;

procedure TForm1.FormCreate(Sender: TObject);
begin
  OpenCom(pchar('com2:9600,N,8,1'));
  Timer1.Interval := 500;
  Timer1.Enabled := true;
  Resolution := 1
end;
```

*continued on following page ...*

```
procedure TForm1.Timer1Timer(Sender: TObject);
var Voltage: Real;
begin
  Case Resolution of
  1: begin
       Voltage := Frequency(100)/10*Calibration;
       Edit1.Text := FloatToStrF(Voltage,ffGeneral,3,0) + ' mV';
     end;
  2: begin
       Voltage := Frequency(1000)/10*Calibration;
       Edit1.Text := FloatToStrF(Voltage,ffGeneral,5,1) + ' mV';
     end;
  3: begin
       Voltage := Frequency(10000)/10*Calibration;
       Edit1.Text := FloatToStrF(Voltage,ffGeneral,6,2) + ' mV';
     end;
  end;
end;

procedure TForm1.RadioButton1Click(Sender: TObject);
begin
  Timer1.Interval := 1000;
  Resolution := 1
end;

procedure TForm1.RadioButton2Click(Sender: TObject);
begin
  Timer1.Interval := 1500;
  Resolution := 2
end;

procedure TForm1.RadioButton3Click(Sender: TObject);
begin
  Timer1.Interval := 12000;
  Resolution := 3
end;

end.
```

## 6.4 Frequency plotter

Analogue measurements are much more accurately transferred in the form of digital signals. When a voltage is first converted into a proportional frequency, the signal can be transmitted very simply via an optocoupler or a fibre optic cable. This achieves complete isolation at low cost. A typical application for isolated measurements is ECG voltage recording. The signal must be decoupled because of the essential safety requirements of electrical isolation and suppression of 50/60-Hz mains-frequency interference.

The recording requires the acquisition of faster changes of signal voltage. The previous frequency measurement is inappropriate because of its long gate time. However, here a measurement of the cycle period is applied, from which the frequency can be simply computed. As the achievable resolution is closely coupled to the time resolution under Windows, one must work with relatively low frequencies and long cycle periods. Favourable frequencies are approximately 100 Hz, and the present program limits the measurement range to between 50 Hz and 200 Hz.

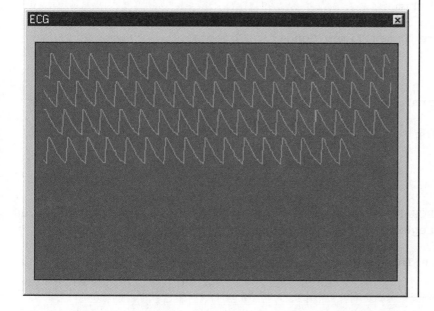

*Figure 6.7*
*Recording of a*
*test signal*

*Listing 6.4*

*ECG recording of frequency measurement*

The program ECG plots several curves together on one sheet, enabling a sufficiently longer period to be observed. The measurement interval is controlled over the timer with a duration of 20 ms. The main measurement function FQ measures the period at the DSR input every 20 ms. It first waits for the positive edge of the input signal. Following this comes a time measurement for each phase of the input signal, thus measuring the time delay to the next positive edge. The measured interval is divided by 1,000,000 μsec to provide the frequency in Hertz.

```
unit ecg;
interface
uses   PortInc,
   Windows, Messages, SysUtils, Classes, Graphics, Controls,
   Forms, Dialogs, StdCtrls, ExtCtrls;

type
   TForm1 = class(TForm)
      PaintBox1: TPaintBox;
      Timer1: TTimer;
      procedure FormCreate(Sender: TObject);
      procedure Timer1Timer(Sender: TObject);
   end;

var
   Form1: TForm1;

implementation

{$R *.DFM}

var
      Buffer:PCHAR;
      Size:Integer;
      n: word;
var i,x,y,w,h:Integer;
```

*continued on following page ...*

```
function Fq: Integer;
var Counter: word;
begin
  RealTime (true);
  TimeInitus;
  if (DSR=1) then while ((TimeReadus < 20000) and (DSR=1)) do;
  TimeInitUs;
  while ((TimeReadus < 20000) and (DSR=0)) do;
   TimeInitUs;
  while ((TimeReadus < 10000) and (DSR=1)) do;
  while ((TimeReadus < 20000) and (DSR=0)) do;
  Counter := TimeReadus;
  If Counter > 20000 Then Counter := 20000;
  If Counter < 5000 then Counter := 5000;
  RealTime (false);
  Fq := 1000000 div Counter;
end;

procedure TForm1.FormCreate(Sender: TObject);
begin
   OpenCom(pchar('com2:9600,N,8,1'));
   RTS (1);
   Size:=paintbox1.width;
   GetMem(Buffer,Size+1);
   for n:=0 to size-1 do buffer[n]:=#127;
   n:=0;
end;

procedure TForm1.Timer1Timer(Sender: TObject);
var u:Integer;
begin
  {u:= 20+round(20*sin(n/5)) + 20* (n div 380);   }
  u:= fq div 4 + 30* (n div 380);
  if n=0 then begin;
  w:=paintbox1.width;
  h:=paintbox1.height;
  Paintbox1.Canvas.Pen.Color:=ClBlack;
  Paintbox1.Canvas.Brush.Color:=ClGreen;
```

*continued on following page ...*

```
   PaintBox1.Canvas.Rectangle(0,0,w,h);
   paintbox1.canvas.pen.color:=cllime;
     x:= 10;
   paintbox1.canvas.MoveTo(x,u);
   end else begin
     x:=10+ n mod 380;
     paintbox1.canvas.LineTo(x,u);
     if x=389 then paintbox1.canvas.MoveTo(9,u+30);
   end;
   n:= n+1;
   if n= 3800 then n:=0;
end;

end.
```

# Synchronous Serial Data Transmission

The serial interface normally works as an asynchronous RS-232 device, where individual data bits are packed in equal length pulses and sequentially transmitted over the TxD line. The receiving device must be aware of the time frame and must also wait for the beginning of each and every transmission. These operations impose high demands on the receive circuitry. Benefit can be taken, at minimal cost, from the advantages of serial data transmission by introducing additional clock pulses for the receiver shown below.

## 7.1 Serial output

The data receiver needs primarily a shift register, this being an integrated circuit with typically eight consecutively chained flip-flops, the logical status of which is shifted using a common clock signal. The variable status of the first data input is then shifted bit-wise into the eight flip-flops, such that serial data is transformed into parallel data. The required clock signal to control simple shift registers must be generated from the transmission program itself, as the serial PC interface hardware does not provide any clock signal.

Figure 7.1 shows the connection of one or more 4094 CMOS shift registers. It can be seen that besides the data and clock signals, one additional line is introduced. This is because the 4094

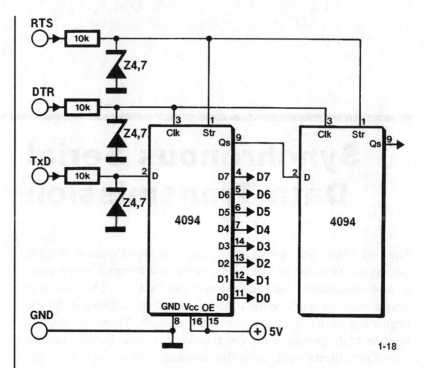

*Figure 7.1*

*Data transmission via CD4094 shift registers*

has integrated storage registers to transfer all received bits to the outputs. For this an additional strobe pulse is needed, which has to be generated by the PC at the end of any 8 bit transmission.

The output voltage of lines TxD, RTS and DTR exceed the nominal input voltage of the CMOS IC's. By using both resistors and Zener diodes, the voltage is limited to the range of 0–5 V. Alternatively, high-value(100-k$\Omega$) resistors can be inserted and the Zener diodes omitted, the voltage limitation then being handled by the CMOS chip internal diodes.

Listing 7.1 shows the output procedure for the clocked, serial data transmission. Different to normal asynchronous transmission, the data bits on the TxD line are directly generated by the program. The required clock pulse is generated by switching the DTR line on and off. In addition to the eight pulses, a strobe pulse is generated on the RTS line.

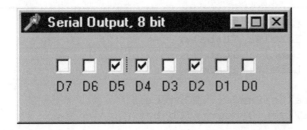

*Figure 7.2*

*Controlling output states*

The program contains time delays of 10 μs to ensure that no time overlapping of the pulses can occur, and that the pulses are sufficiently long. Too fast an output can lead to transmission errors as the IC has a maximum clock rate of 2 MHz at a supply voltage of 5 V. The rate or rise of the PC RS232 interface lines is also limited, so pulses that are too short could be suppressed.

The program SHIFT1 uses eight check boxes, which can be used to change the output status of each 4094 shift register. The virtual data transmission follows ten times per second, defined by the chosen interval of Timers1. The shift register can be used to control up to eight independent loads by the PC when using appropriate drivers. With direct control of procedure OUTPUT, switch events can permit automatic control.

*Listing 7.1*

*Outputting 8-bit values via a shift register*

```
unit Shift1;

interface

uses PORTINC,Windows, Messages, SysUtils, Classes,
Graphics, Controls, Forms, Dialogs, ExtCtrls, StdCtrls;

type
  TForm1 = class(TForm)
    CheckBox1: TCheckBox; CheckBox2: TCheckBox;
    CheckBox3: TCheckBox; CheckBox4: TCheckBox;
    CheckBox5: TCheckBox; CheckBox6: TCheckBox;
    CheckBox7: TCheckBox; CheckBox8: TCheckBox;
```

***continued on following page . . .***

```
      Label1: TLabel; Label2: TLabel;
      Label3: TLabel; Label4: TLabel;
      Label5: TLabel; Label6: TLabel;
      Label7: TLabel; Label8: TLabel;
      Timer1: TTimer;
      procedure FormCreate(Sender: TObject);
      procedure Timer1Timer(Sender: TObject);
    end;

var
    Form1: TForm1;

implementation

{$R *.DFM}

procedure Distribute ( Value : Byte );
var Location, n : Integer;
begin
    Location := 1;
    for n:=1 to 8 do begin
      if ((Value AND Location) > 0) then
        TXD(1)                       { Data on TxD    }
          else TXD(0);
      Delayus(10);                   { Time Delay }
      DTR (1);                       { Clock on  (DTR) }
      Location := Location * 2;
      Delayus(10);                   { Time Delay }
      DTR (0);                       { Clock off (DTR) }
    end;
    RTS (1);                         { Strobe on (RTS) }
      Delayus(10);                   { Time Delay }
    RTS (0);                         { Strobe off(RTS) }
end;

procedure TForm1.FormCreate(Sender: TObject);
begin
    OpenCom(pchar('com2:9600,N,8,1'));
    Timer1.Interval := 100;
    Timer1.Enabled := true;
end;
```

*continued on following page ...*

```
procedure TForm1.Timer1Timer(Sender: TObject);
var Value: Byte;
begin
  Value := 0;
  if  CheckBox1.Checked Then Value := Value +1;
  if  CheckBox2.Checked Then Value := Value +2;
  if  CheckBox3.Checked Then Value := Value +4;
  if  CheckBox4.Checked Then Value := Value +8;
  if  CheckBox5.Checked Then Value := Value +16;
  if  CheckBox6.Checked Then Value := Value +32;
  if  CheckBox7.Checked Then Value := Value +64;
  if  CheckBox8.Checked Then Value := Value +128;
  Distribute(Value);
end;

end.
```

Often, it is necessary to use more than eight output lines, and for this purpose, shift registers can be cascaded. The 4094 places on its output 'Q' pins, serial data for the next chip to read (see Figure 7.1). Next, the necessary control program must clock all bits in the shift register and output a strobe pulse for both chips. Listing 7.2 shows a procedure for serial output with two shift registers, and here a 16 bit word must be handed over. It must be borne in mind, that the eight low significant bits will be transferred into the second IC as they are shifted out first.

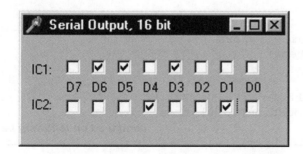

*Figure 7.3*

*Output on two shift registers*

**Listing 7.2** *Program for serial output of two bytes*

```
unit Shift2;

interface

uses PORTINC,Windows, Messages, SysUtils, Classes, Graphics,
      Controls, Forms, Dialogs, ExtCtrls, StdCtrls;

type
   TForm1 = class(TForm)
      CheckBox1: TCheckBox; CheckBox2: TCheckBox;
      CheckBox3: TCheckBox; CheckBox4: TCheckBox;
      CheckBox5: TCheckBox; CheckBox6: TCheckBox;
      CheckBox7: TCheckBox; CheckBox8: TCheckBox;
      Label1: TLabel; Label2: TLabel;
      Label3: TLabel; Label4: TLabel;
      Label5: TLabel; Label6: TLabel;
      Label7: TLabel; Label8: TLabel;
      Timer1: TTimer; Label9: TLabel;
      CheckBox9: TCheckBox; CheckBox10: TCheckBox;
      CheckBox11: TCheckBox; CheckBox12: TCheckBox;
      CheckBox13: TCheckBox; CheckBox14: TCheckBox;
      CheckBox15: TCheckBox; CheckBox16: TCheckBox;
      Label10: TLabel;
      procedure FormCreate(Sender: TObject);
      procedure Timer1Timer(Sender: TObject);
   end;

var
   Form1: TForm1;

implementation

{$R *.DFM}

procedure Output ( Value : Word );
var Location, n : Integer;
begin
   Location := 1;
   for n:=1 to 16 do begin
      if ((Value AND Location) > 0) then
```

*continued on following page ...*

```
      TXD(1)                     { Data on TxD      }
      else TXD(0);
   Delayus(10);                  { Time Delay }
   DTR (1);                      { Clock on   (DTR) }
   Location := Location * 2;
   Delayus(10);                  { Time Delay }
   DTR (0);                      { Clock off (DTR) }
  end;
  RTS (1);                       { Strobe on (RTS) }
    Delayus(10);                 { Time Delay }
  RTS (0);                       { Strobe off (RTS) }
end;

procedure TForm1.FormCreate(Sender: TObject);
begin
  OpenCom(pchar('com2:9600,N,8,1'));
  Timer1.Interval := 100;
  Timer1.Enabled := true;
end;

procedure TForm1.Timer1Timer(Sender: TObject);
var Value: Word;
begin
  Value := 0;
  if   CheckBox1.Checked Then Value := Value +256;
  if   CheckBox2.Checked Then Value := Value +512;
  if   CheckBox3.Checked Then Value := Value +1024;
  if   CheckBox4.Checked Then Value := Value +2048;
  if   CheckBox5.Checked Then Value := Value +4096;
  if   CheckBox6.Checked Then Value := Value +8192;
  if   CheckBox7.Checked Then Value := Value +16384;
  if   CheckBox8.Checked Then Value := Value +32768;
  if   CheckBox9.Checked Then Value := Value +1;
  if   CheckBox10.Checked Then Value := Value +2;
  if   CheckBox11.Checked Then Value := Value +4;
  if   CheckBox12.Checked Then Value := Value +8;
  if   CheckBox13.Checked Then Value := Value +16;
  if   CheckBox14.Checked Then Value := Value +32;
  if   CheckBox15.Checked Then Value := Value +64;
  if   CheckBox16.Checked Then Value := Value +128;
  Output(Value);
end;

end.
```

## 7.2 Serial input

Operation of serial, shifted data transmission can also be used for input purposes. For this a shift register is needed which can be loaded with parallel data, and from which serial data is transmitted. The CD4021 is designed for this operation, and Figure 7.4 shows a connection to the serial interface. The data is read in using the function 'Read' in Listing 7.3 with the speed of generation clock pulses on DCD.

*Figure 7.4*

*8-bit input port with a shift register*

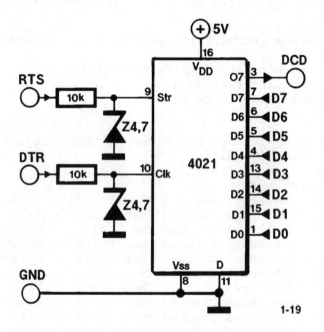

A strobe pulse at the input Str controls the transfer of the input levels into the shift register, and Bit 7 is then available from output Q7. The remaining bits can be shifted to output C7, using the clock pulse on input Clk.

The program Shift3 reads the shift registers' eight input lines and displays the status in Checkboxes. The read operation is repeated every 100 ms in accordance with Timer1, and the program can supervise eight independent input states.

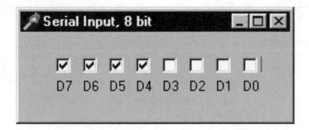

*Figure 7.5*
*Read-in*
*shift register*
*states*

*Listing 7.3*
*Program to*
*read data*
*serially from a*
*shift register*

```
unit Shift3;

interface

uses PORTINC,
   Windows, Messages, SysUtils, Classes, Graphics, Controls,
   Forms, Dialogs, ExtCtrls, StdCtrls;

type
   TForm1 = class(TForm)
      CheckBox1: TCheckBox;   CheckBox2: TCheckBox;
      CheckBox3: TCheckBox;   CheckBox4: TCheckBox;
      CheckBox5: TCheckBox;   CheckBox6: TCheckBox;
      CheckBox7: TCheckBox;   CheckBox8: TCheckBox;
      Label1: TLabel;   Label2: TLabel;
      Label3: TLabel;   Label4: TLabel;
      Label5: TLabel;   Label6: TLabel;
      Label7: TLabel;   Label8: TLabel;
      Timer1: TTimer;
      procedure FormCreate(Sender: TObject);
      procedure Timer1Timer(Sender: TObject);
   end;

var
   Form1: TForm1;

implementation

{$R *.DFM}
```

*continued on following page ...*

```
function Read: Byte;
var Location, n : Integer;
    Receive : Byte;
begin
  RTS(1);                       { Strobe an }
  Delayus(10);                  { Time Delay }
  RTS (0);               { Strobe off }
  Location := 1;
  Receive:= 0;
  for n:=1 to 8 do begin
    Delayus(10);        { Time Delay }
    if DCD=1                 { Data read }
       then Receive:= Receive + Location;
    DTR (1);                 { Clock on }
    Location := Location * 2;
    Delayus(10);          { Time Delay }
    DTR (0);                  { Clock off }
  end;
  Read := Receive;
end;

procedure TForm1.FormCreate(Sender: TObject);
begin
  OpenCom(pchar('com2:9600,N,8,1'));
  Timer1.Interval := 100;
  Timer1.Enabled := true;
end;

procedure TForm1.Timer1Timer(Sender: TObject);
var Value: Byte;
begin
  Value := Read;
  CheckBox1.Checked := (Value And 1) > 0;
  CheckBox2.Checked := (Value And 2) > 0;
  CheckBox3.Checked := (Value And 4) > 0;
  CheckBox4.Checked := (Value And 8) > 0;
  CheckBox5.Checked := (Value And 16) > 0;
  CheckBox6.Checked := (Value And 32) > 0;
  CheckBox7.Checked := (Value And 64) > 0;
  CheckBox8.Checked := (Value And 128) > 0;
end;

end.
```

## 7.3 Serial A/D converter

The Texas Instruments TLC549 is a cost-effective A/D converter which possess a shift register read in a similar manner to the 4021. The virtual conversion of a voltage into an 8-bit byte needs little more than 20 µsec, enabling faster measurement. The IC needs a chip select signal to change, between conversion and output modes. It is treated in a similar manner as the 4021 strobe signal.

Figure 7.6 shows a connection of the converter to the serial interface with the 5 V supply used as a reference voltage. With a resolution of 256 possible voltage values, a difference of circa 20 mV is recognised. The reference voltage is also often fixed at 2.55 V, providing accurate 10-mV steps.

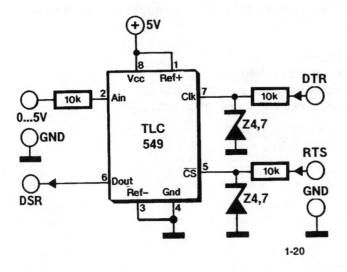

*Figure 7.6*

*Connecting a TLC549 A/D converter to the serial interface*

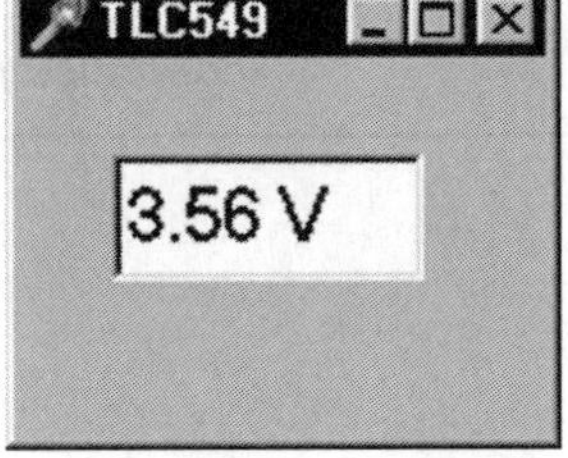

*Figure 7.7*

*Displaying the measured voltage*

Listing 7.4 shows the function 'AD' which enables simple access from the A/D converter. The conversion takes place while the /CS line is in the high state and approximately 20 μs is needed for this. When CS again descends, the highest significant data bit first appears on the data line. With each clock pulse, the next lower significant bit is shifted out. The data bit sequencing of the A/D converter therefore differs to the one used with the shift registers above.

*Listing 7.4*

*Program for voltage measurement with the TLC549*

```
unit TLC549;
interface
uses PORTINC, Windows, Messages, SysUtils, Classes,
   Graphics, Controls, Forms, Dialogs, StdCtrls, ExtCtrls;

type
   TForm1 = class(TForm)
     Timer1: TTimer; Edit1: TEdit;
     procedure FormCreate(Sender: TObject);
     procedure Timer1Timer(Sender: TObject);
   end;

var
   Form1: TForm1;

implementation

{$R *.DFM}

function AD : Byte;
var n, Location : Integer;
     Value : Byte;
```

*continued on following page ...*

```
begin
  RTS (1);                    { /CS on }
  Delayus(10);                { Time Delay }
  RTS (0);                    { /CS off }
  Delayus(10);                { Time Delay }
  Value := 0;
  Location := 128;
  for n:= 1 to 8 do begin
    if DSR = 1 then           { Data read }
    Value := Value + Location;
    DTR (1);                  { Clock on }
    Delayus(10);              { Time Delay }
    DTR (0);                  { Clock off }
    Location := Location div 2;
  end;
  AD := Value;
end;

procedure TForm1.FormCreate(Sender: TObject);
begin
  OpenCom(pchar('com2:9600,N,8,1'));
  Timer1.Interval := 100;
  Timer1.Enabled := true;
end;

procedure TForm1.Timer1Timer(Sender: TObject);
var Voltage: Real;
begin
  Voltage:= AD/255*5;
  Edit1.Text := FloatToStrF(Voltage,ffGeneral,3,2) + ' V';
end;

end.
```

# A Multi-purpose Interface

Even though the number of available lines on the serial interface is limited, several of the previously described interfacing methods (see Chapter 7) can be combined to construct a multi-purpose interface.

## 8.1 Hardware and its control

Figure 8.1 shows an interface block diagram with eight digital outputs, eight digital inputs, an analogue input and a frequency input. All three shift registers for I/O can be controlled by a single clock line and a single strobe line.

I/O can be processed simultaneously, with a common clock signal being applied to all chips. The procedure 'Exchange' in Listing 8.1 controls bi-directional data transmission. Each call refreshes the 4094 output status and at the same time reads the digital inputs status and the A/D converter. Data is stored in the global variables Dout (digital output), Din (digital input) and Ain (analogue input).

In addition, the free CTS input is available for frequency measurement. The gate time is always set to 100ms, so that it gives a frequency resolution from 10 Hz. If the voltage-frequency converter is added, then the interface can be provided with two analogue inputs.

**Figure 8.1**
*Multi-purpose
serial interface*

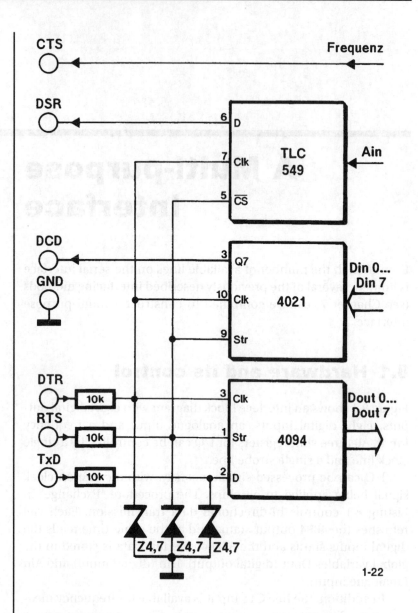

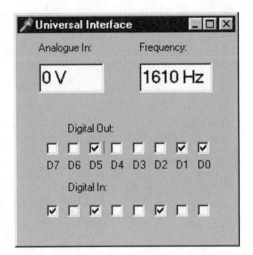

*Figure 8.2*
*Universal Interface control*

*Listing 8.1*
*Basic program for the serial multi-purpose interface*

```
unit Uni1;

interface

uses PORTINC, Windows, Messages, SysUtils, Classes, Graphics,
     Controls, Forms, Dialogs, ExtCtrls, StdCtrls;

type
  TForm1 = class(TForm)
    CheckBox1: TCheckBox; CheckBox2: TCheckBox;
    CheckBox3: TCheckBox; CheckBox4: TCheckBox;
    CheckBox5: TCheckBox; CheckBox6: TCheckBox;
    CheckBox7: TCheckBox; CheckBox8: TCheckBox;
    Label1: TLabel; Label2: TLabel;
    Label3: TLabel; Label4: TLabel;
    Label5: TLabel; Label6: TLabel;
    Label7: TLabel; Label8: TLabel;
    Timer1: TTimer; Label9: TLabel;
    CheckBox9: TCheckBox; CheckBox10: TCheckBox;
    CheckBox11: TCheckBox; CheckBox12: TCheckBox;
    CheckBox13: TCheckBox; CheckBox14: TCheckBox;
    CheckBox15: TCheckBox; CheckBox16: TCheckBox;
    Label10: TLabel; Edit1: TEdit;
    Label11: TLabel; Edit2: TEdit;
    Label12: TLabel;
    procedure FormCreate(Sender: TObject);
    procedure Timer1Timer(Sender: TObject);
  end;
```

**continued on following page ...**

```
var
   Form1: TForm1;
   Dout, Din, Ain: Byte;

implementation

{$R *.DFM}

procedure Exchange;
var Location, Location, n, m   : Integer;
begin
   RTS (1);                              { Strobe on }
   Delayus(20);                               { Time Delay }
   RTS (0);                              { Strobe off }
   Location := 1;
   LocationAD := 128;
   Din := 0;
   Ain := 0;
   for n:=1 to 8 do begin
     if ((Dout AND Location) > 0) then
        TXD (1)                          { Data output }
        else TXD (0);
     if DCD = 1                          { Data read }
        then Din := Din + Location;
     if DSR = 1 then                     { A/D read }
        Ain := Ain + LocationAD;
     DTR (1);                            { Clock on }
   Delayus(20);                          { Time Delay }
     DTR (0);                            { Clock off }
     Location := Location * 2;
     LocationAD := LocationAD div 2;
   end;
   RTS (1);                              { Strobe on }
   Delayus(20);                               { Time Delay }
   RTS (0);                              { Strobe off }
end;

function Frequency: Integer;
var Counter, old, Input : Integer;
begin
   Counter := 0;
   RealTime (true);
   TimeInitus;
   old:=CTS;
```

*continued on following page ...*

```
  while TimeReadus < (100000) do begin
    Input := CTS;
    if Input> old then Counter := Counter +1;
    Old := Input;
  end;
  Frequency := Counter;
  RealTime (false);
end;

procedure TForm1.FormCreate(Sender: TObject);
begin
  OpenCom(pchar('com2:9600,N,8,1'));
  Timer1.Interval := 100;
  Timer1.Enabled := true;
end;

procedure TForm1.Timer1Timer(Sender: TObject);
var Value: Word;
    Voltage: Real;
begin
  Dout := 0;
  if   CheckBox1.Checked Then Dout := Dout +1;
  if   CheckBox2.Checked Then Dout := Dout +2;
  if   CheckBox3.Checked Then Dout := Dout +4;
  if   CheckBox4.Checked Then Dout := Dout +8;
  if   CheckBox5.Checked Then Dout := Dout +16;
  if   CheckBox6.Checked Then Dout := Dout +32;
  if   CheckBox7.Checked Then Dout := Dout +64;
  if   CheckBox8.Checked Then Dout := Dout +128;
  Exchange;
  CheckBox9.Checked := ((Din And 1) >0);
  CheckBox10.Checked := ((Din And 2) >0);
  CheckBox11.Checked := ((Din And 4) >0);
  CheckBox12.Checked := ((Din And 8) >0);

  CheckBox13.Checked := ((Din And 16) >0);
  CheckBox14.Checked := ((Din And 32) >0);
  CheckBox15.Checked := ((Din And 64) >0);
  CheckBox16.Checked := ((Din And 128) >0);
  Voltage := Ain/255*5;
  Edit1.Text := FloatToStrF(Voltage,ffGeneral,3,2) + ' V';
  Edit2.Text := FloatToStrF(Frequency*10,ffGeneral,4,0) + '
      Hz';
end;

end.
```

## 8.2 The Compact Universal program

For the various circuits in electronic construction the versatile application COMPACT has been developed in the Delphi language. It controls all the universal interface I/O and permits flexible reception of measurement values. The COM interface can be chosen in the application start-up screen. The program can be found in *.exe format on the CD.

*Figure 8.3*
*Compact*
*Universal*
*program*

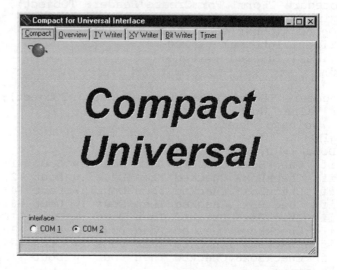

The start dialogue has several tabs for various functions. The 'Overview' tab gives direct access to all input and output functions. Analogue inputs for both voltage and frequency are displayed in a software instrument panel. There is also a digital display that shows the byte provided by the A/D converter for the voltage input. Measuring equipment can be used both directly for experiments, and for monitoring electronic functions.

In addition to the analogue inputs, the Universal Interface also has fast acting digital I/O. The eight digital inputs are simultaneously displayed both as virtual LEDs and as a digital report with a corresponding byte values between 0 and 255. The status of a digital switch can also be directly supervised, and the digital outputs are changed using virtual slide switches. A digital display shows the complete port state as a single byte.

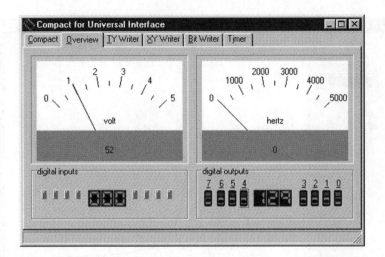

**Figure 8.4**

*Direct display of I/O*

The basic function 'Overview' conforms in its fundamental functions with part of the UNI1.EXE program, as per previous Chapters. Additional possibilities are apparent with several types of plotters in the program.

The Y–T plotter plots one or both analogue input quantities versus time. The observation of time dependent quantities is therefore quite simple. The measurement period is chosen in a range between one second and 24 hours.

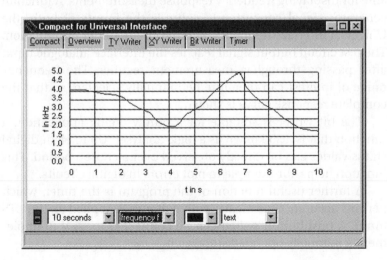

**Figure 8.5**

*Measured values plotter*

**Figure 8.6**

*The X–Y plotter*

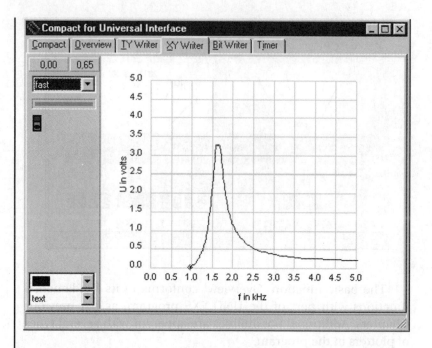

Analogue quantities are often mutually dependent, therefore an X–Y plotter is provided. Using Compact Universal, voltage can be plotted against frequency, and these plots are particularly suitable for displaying frequency response measurements. A function generator signal concurrently controls the inputs of both, the Universal Interface frequency, and the circuit under examination. The test circuit output signal reaches the interface analogue input after passing through a measurement rectifier. The frequency range of interest can therefore be manually selected, so that the complete response curve is shown.

The bit writer is suitable for a purely digital application, a function that is also known as a logic analyser. Up to eight digital status values can be directly observed over a chosen period. This function helps, for example to plot errors in digital circuits.

A further useful function of the program is the timer, which permits accurate time measurement of pulses applied to the CTS input. A pushbutton switch can be connected to +5 V to implement a manually operated stopwatch.

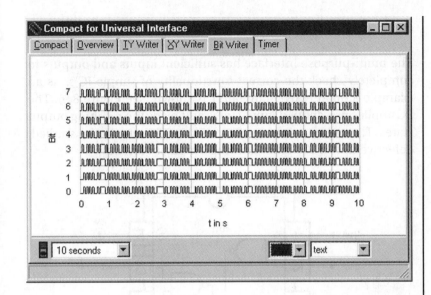

*Figure 8.7*
*Digital writer*

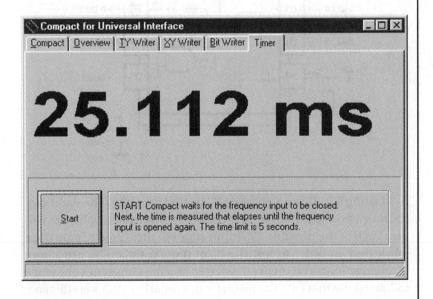

*Figure 8.8*
*Time*
*measurement*
*in Compact*

## 8.3 Automatic IC tester

The multi-purpose interface has sufficient inputs and outputs to completely check the correct functionality of simple IC's. As an example a quad NAND-chip 4011 is shown (see Figure 8.9). The PC applies pre-defined input states and reads the resulting output states. The current-sinking of candidate IC's can also be studied, defective CMOS ICs often drawing a greater current.

*Figure 8.9*

*CMOS chip testing using the multi-purpose interface*

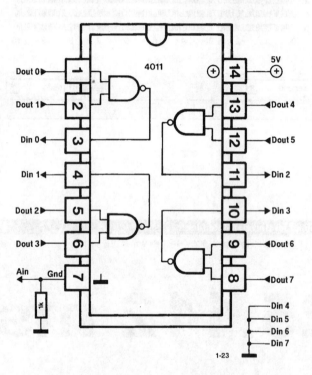

Listing 8.2 shows a possible IC testing program. The eight digital outputs of the interface are counted upwards using binary values. Each of the possible 256 input states of the tested ICs are once fabricated, in order to test the IC outputs results. The procedure 'Exchange' must be invoked twice each time consecutively, while following the first call, the result from the earlier status is still read.

This time-consuming calculation of correct output status is redundant when reference tables are used. Clicking the button 'New' with a new IC as test candidate generates these tables. A table can be saved or loaded as a binary file, for example CD4011.BIN. These test methods can be simply extended to further ICs, where a specific data table is loaded for each new IC. Using suitable test sockets, various ICs can be tested, each known deviation from a normal function leading to an error message. This applies also to an increased current consumption greater than 0.2 mA.

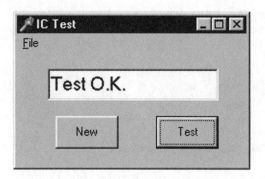

*Figure 8.10*
*IC tester*

*Listing 8.2*
*test program*
*for a 4011*
*CMOS chip*

```
unit ICtest;

interface

uses PORTINC, Windows, Messages, SysUtils, Classes,
Graphics, Controls, Forms, Dialogs, ExtCtrls, StdCtrls, Menus;

type
  TForm1 = class(TForm)
    Edit1: TEdit; Button1: TButton;
    Button2: TButton; Timer1: TTimer;
    OpenDialog1: TOpenDialog; SaveDialog1: TSaveDialog;
    MainMenu1: TMainMenu; File1: TMenuItem;
    SaveAs1: TMenuItem; Open1: TMenuItem;
    New1: TMenuItem;
    procedure FormCreate(Sender: TObject);
```
**continued on following page ...**

# 8  A Multi-purpose Interface

```
      procedure Button3Click(Sender: TObject);
      procedure Button2Click(Sender: TObject);
      procedure Button1Click(Sender: TObject);
      procedure Timer1Timer(Sender: TObject);
      procedure Open1Click(Sender: TObject);
      procedure SaveAs1Click(Sender: TObject);
    end;

var
    Form1: TForm1;
    Dout, Din, Ain: Byte;
    n: Integer;
    Characteristics: Array[0..255] of Byte;
    Testfile: File of Byte;
    Filename: String;

implementation

{$R *.DFM}

procedure Exchange;
var Location, LocationAD, n, m   : Integer;
begin
    RTS (1);                             { Strobe on }
    Delayus(20);                         { Time delay }
    RTS (0);                             { Strobe off }
    Location := 1;
    LocationAD := 128;
    Din := 0;
    Ain := 0;
    for n:=1 to 8 do begin
      if ((Dout AND Location) > 0) then
        TXD (1)                          { Data distribution }
        else TXD (0);
      if DCD = 1                         { Data read }
        then Din := Din + Location;
      if DSR = 1 then                    { A/D read }
        Ain := Ain + SLocationAD;
      DTR (1);                           { Clock on }
    Delayus(20);                         { Time delay }
      DTR (0);                           { Clock off }
```

*continued on following page ...*

```
    Location := Location * 2;
    LocationAD := LocationAD div 2;
  end;
  RTS (1);                              { Strobe on }
  Delayus(20);                          { Time delay }
  RTS (0);                              { Strobe off }
end;
procedure TForm1.FormCreate(Sender: TObject);
begin
  OpenCom(pchar('com2:9600,N,8,1'));
end;

procedure TForm1.Button3Click(Sender: TObject);
var n: Integer;
begin
{Filename := OpenDialog.FileName;}
Filename := 'TEST.BIN';
AssignFile (Testfile,Filename);
{$I-} Rewrite (Testfile) {$I+};
for n:= 0 to 255 do begin;
  write (Testfile, Characteristics[n]);
end;
CloseFile (Testfile);
end;

procedure TForm1.Button2Click(Sender: TObject);
var Value: Word;
    Voltage, Error : Real;
begin
  Timer1.Enabled := false;
  Error := 0;
  Edit1.Text := 'Test ...';
  for n := 1 to 255 do begin
    Dout := n;
    Exchange;
    Delay (1);
    Exchange;
    If (Ain > 10) or (Din <> Characteristics[n]) then begin
      Error := Error + 1;
      Voltage := Ain/255*5;
      Edit1.Text := FloatToStr(N) + ', ' +
```

*continued on following page ...*

```
      FloatToStr(Din) + '<> '+FloatToStr(Characteristics[n]) +
      '  '+ FloatToStrF(Voltage,ffGeneral,3,2) + ' mA';
    end;
  end;
  If Error = 0 then Edit1.Text := 'Test O.K.';
  Timer1.Interval := 2000;
  Timer1.Enabled := true;
end;

procedure TForm1.Button1Click(Sender: TObject);
var n: Integer;
begin
{Filename := OpenDialog.FileName;}
Timer1.Enabled := false;
for n:= 0 to 255 do begin;
  Dout := n;
  Exchange;
  Delay (1);
  Exchange;
  Exchange[n] := Din;
end;
Edit1.text := 'Ready';
Timer1.Enabled := true;
end;
procedure TForm1.Timer1Timer(Sender: TObject);
begin
  Edit1.Text := 'range';
  Timer1.Enabled := false
end;

procedure TForm1.Open1Click(Sender: TObject);
begin
  OpenDialog1.FileName := '*.bin';
  OpenDialog1.Execute;
  Filename := OpenDialog1.FileName;
  if Filename > '' then begin
    AssignFile (Testfile,Filename);
    {$I-} Reset (Testfile) {$I+};
    for n:= 0 to 255 do read (Testfile,Characteristics[n]);
    CloseFile (Testfile);
  end
end;
```

*continued on following page ...*

```
procedure TForm1.SaveAs1Click(Sender: TObject);
  var n: Integer;
begin
  SaveDialog1.FileName := '*.bin';
  SaveDialog1.Execute;
  Filename := SaveDialog1.FileName;
  If Filename > '' then begin
    AssignFile (Testfile,Filename);
    {$I-} Rewrite (Testfile) {$I+};
    for n:= 0 to 255 do write (Testfile, Characteristics[n]);
    CloseFile (Testfile);
  end;
end;

end.
```

# The Parallel Printer Port

The PC parallel interface, LPT1 or LPT2, provides a total of 17 digital lines, making it useful for fast data exchange with interface circuits. Using these 17 lines, a few experiments are especially simple, however use of the printer interface demands particular care. In contrast to the serial interface it can be inadvertently destroyed with relative ease, as all parallel port I/O lines are unprotected against overload. The following health regulations must be observed:

* Parallel port equipment can only be connected to a powered down PC.
* Input voltages must be maintained between 0 V and 5 V.
* Outputs cannot be shorted or connected to other outputs.
* Outputs must never be connected to the supply voltage of other equipment.

## 9.1 I/O lines

The following diagram shows all the connections. Figure 9.1 shows the pin assignments of a 25-way sub-D plug for the PC. As well as this, a 36-way Centronics socket can be used with a normal printer cable. Unfortunately, purchased printer cables do not always fully match the illustrated connections, so it is recommended to first carefully check the cable before using it.

| Pin 25-P | Pin 36-P | Designation | Access | Data Direction |
|----------|----------|-------------|--------|----------------|
| 2 | 2 | D0 | BA, Bit 0 | Output |
| 3 | 3 | D1 | BA, Bit 1 | Output |
| 9 | 9 | D7 | BA, Bit 7 | Output |
| 15 | 32 | Error | BA+1, Bit 3 | Input |
| 13 | 13 | Select | BA+1, Bit 4 | Input |
| 12 | 12 | PE | BA+1, Bit 5 | Input |
| 10 | 10 | ACK | BA+1, Bit 6 | Input |
| 11 | 11 | Busy | BA+1, Bit 7 | Input, inverted |
| 1 | 1 | Strobe | BA+2, Bit 0 | I/O, inverted |
| 14 | 14 | Auto Feed | BA+2, Bit 1 | I/O, inverted |
| 16 | 31 | Init | BA+2, Bit 2 | I/O |
| 17 | 36 | SLCT IN | BA+2, Bit 3 | I/O, inverted |

**Figure 9.1**

*Parallel interface pin assignments
at the PC and printer*

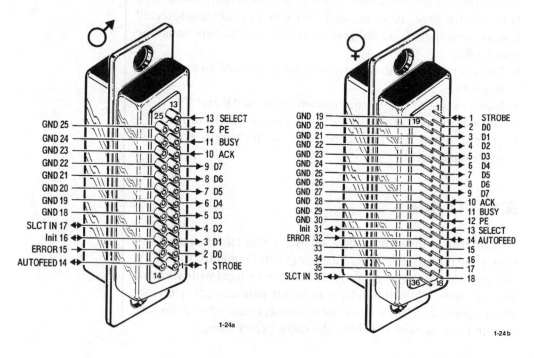

The interface allocation uses the base address (BA) and both the following addresses:

| Register | Offset | Comments |
|----------|--------|----------|
| Data | 0 | Printer data output |
| Status | 1 | Printer status read |
| Control | 2 | Printer function control |

Data register (offset = 0)

| 7 | 6 | 5 | 4 | 3 | 2 | 1 | 0 |
|---|---|---|---|---|---|---|---|

D0–D7 output

Status register (offset = 1)

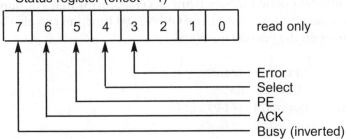

| 7 | 6 | 5 | 4 | 3 | 2 | 1 | 0 |
|---|---|---|---|---|---|---|---|

read only

Error
Select
PE
ACK
Busy (inverted)

Control register (offset = 2)

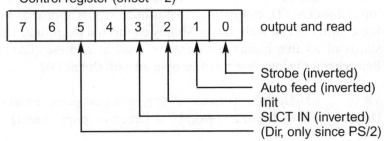

| 7 | 6 | 5 | 4 | 3 | 2 | 1 | 0 |
|---|---|---|---|---|---|---|---|

output and read

Strobe (inverted)
Auto feed (inverted)
Init
SLCT IN (inverted)
(Dir, only since PS/2)

**131**

An additional printer interface to LPT1 is often found, i.e. a second interface, LPT2. In the following programs LPT1 is used. Such interfaces can easily be used with another base address for another printer.

|  | LPT1 | LPT2 |
|---|---|---|
| hexadecimal | 378 | 278 |
| decimal | 888 | 632 |

With the data register a complete 8-bit output port is available, which is normally used to transmit printer data. The output is TTL compatible, that is the high level is between 3.5 V and 5 V, and the output can supply circa 10 mA.

The port is useful for very fast 8-bit output, but the interface must first be opened before being accessed, with that Windows permits the physical output. The OPENCOM function can also be used to open the parallel interface.

```
VB:        OPENCOM ('LPT1:')
           OUTPORT BA,N
Delphi:    OpenCOM ('LPT1:');
           OutPort (BA,N);
```

Of the many printer auxiliary lines there are five inputs represented by the status register, i.e. Error, Select, PE, ACK and Busy, one of which (Busy) is read in the inverted state. Mostly these input lines are TTL compatible, that is open inputs appear as set high. Switches can with that be simply connected to ground. The status of all five inputs lines can be read at address (BA+1). Beforehand the interface must be opened with OpenCOM.

```
VB:        A=INPORT (BA+1) : REM status port read
Delphi:    A:= Inport (BA+1);  {status port read}
```

Port address (BA+2) permits access to the control register with the four auxiliary lines Strobe, Auto Feed, Init and SLCT IN, via which PC normally sends control information to the printer. These four lines can however also be read. Data is output to an open collector output. The pull-up resistors to +5 V are circa 3.3 kΩ. If one outputs a high status the output lines are at high impedance and can easily be pulled down to ground level. The respective status is read back via a TTL input, therefore these four lines can be used for both data directions.  It must be borne in mind that three of these lines (Strobe, Auto Feed and SLCT IN) are inverted, whereas one (Init) is not. In the programs, the bits of interest can easily be inverted using the XOR function, i.e:

VB (output):      OUTPORT BA+2, A XOR 11
VB (input:        B = (INPORT (BA+2) XOR 11) AND 15

Delphi (output):  OutPort (BA+2, A XOR 11);
Delphi (input):   B:= (Inport (BA+2) XOR 11) AND 15;

## 9.2  Bi-directional printer interfaces

The hitherto explained properties of the printer interface are valid for the standard Centronics interface. In modern computers there is an extended printer interface, the ECP or EPP interface, which permits bi-directional data transmission via the 8-bit printer port. These interfaces can always be used in ISA-compatible mode for compatibility with old printer interfaces, that is, with all access functions just as described above.

However, in addition, using ECP and EPP modes there are expanded transmission modes available,  in which addresses and data are sent separately and entire data blocks can be transmitted. Unfortunately the implementation of these enhancement is not particularly simple, with special external circuitry being required for their use. To make matters even more complicated, different chips are used in various PCs, each of which has to be driven in its own particular manner. For example, suitable drivers control data communications with external Zip drives and scanners. In this book these modes are not used, as they appear to be excessively complicated.

There is one advantage of the modern parallel port, i.e. with appropriate software, hobby users can also make use of it. In many cases 8-bit input over the printer port is possible, this being the case, when the interface supports PS/2-compatible mode, as one more control bit is added to the previous standard. Using bit 5 (DIR = 1), the direction of the eight-bit data port can be chosen as either output or read. If an ECP- or EPP-mode interface is installed, the printer port is also PS/2-compatible and supports the input of parallel data.

Whether the interface supports parallel data input can be determined using the following small program in VB5. The data direction can be switched using two buttons. An interface that is only ISA-compatible always reads back the last word that was output. If the interface supports parallel reading, when the data direction is changed to input all data lines are set high and have high impedance. An open port then shows the value '255'.

*Figure 9.2*
*Parallel inputs*
*and outputs*

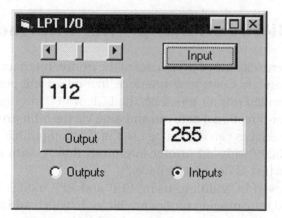

After the data direction is changed to read, lines 2–9 of the printer port have a '1' level, i.e. +5 V. However, they have a relatively high impedance, so they can be pulled down with small currents of approximately 1 mA. A simple read access from the base address provides the actual port state. In this state the interface can be used for parallel input. If it is required to use the printer port for direct input, it is recommended to use additional protection resistors. This is to limit possible short-circuit currents, should the port be switched to the output direction by mistake.

If the interface is used in the output direction, all lines are at low impedance and can source up to 30 mA to ground. Direct interconnections with external switches or logic outputs would be risky. This is usually the state that is present following power-up of the PC. To ensure faster data transfer, modern printer ports use robust industrial output drivers, which are more powerful than the older Centronics interface. The data lines can therefore be used to supply power to low-power circuitry.

*Listing 9.1*

*Bi-directional data traffic test*

```
Dim BA As Integer

Private Sub Command1_Click()
  OUTPORT BA, HScroll1.Value
End Sub

Private Sub Command2_Click()
  D = INPORT(BA)
  D = D And 255
  Text2.Text = Str$(D)
End Sub

Private Sub Form_Load()
  If OPENCOM("LPT1:") = 0 Then MsgBox ("LPT1 not free")
  BA = &H378
  OUTPORT (BA + 2), 0    'Output
End Sub

Private Sub Form_Unload(Cancel As Integer)
  CLOSECOM
End Sub

Private Sub HScroll1_Change()
  Text1.Text = Str$(HScroll1.Value)
End Sub
```

***continued on following page ...***

# 9 The Parallel Printer Port

```
Private Sub Option1_Click()
   OUTPORT (BA + 2), 0   'Output
End Sub

Private Sub Option2_Click()
   OUTPORT (BA + 2), 32   'Input
End Sub
```

# 10

# Parallel Data Output

The printer interface is suitable for parallel 8-bit output, and for example, one can implement various types of control over logic circuits or power drivers. In contrast to serial output, an output via the parallel port is executed with a single command and is thus extremely fast. With this capability, it is even possible to generate low-frequency (audio) analogue signals with high quality.

*Figure10.1*

*Connecting the ZN426 D/A converter to the printer port*

## 10.1 Function generator

A function generator produces ac voltages with variable frequency and selectable waveform. To achieve this with a PC, discrete digital samples of an analogue signal must be generated. To convert a digital to an analogue signal, a digital to analogue converter can be used, for example the Ferranti ZN426. Figure10.1 shows the printer port connection. The chip contains an internal voltage reference of 2.55 V, with which 256 voltage steps from 10 mV can be resolved, and the output voltage reaches from 0 to 2.55 V.

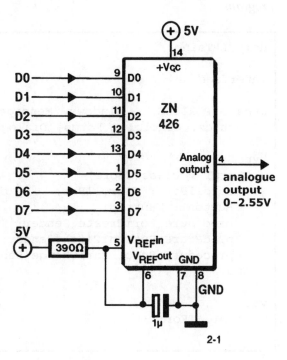

# 10 Parallel Data Output

Listing 10.1 shows a program for an audio frequency sine-wave generator. The program contains a value table, that is initialised using the Start function. During the actual output, values were taken from the prepared sine table. The output speed is adjustable between limits of 10 µs and 1 ms using a slider bar, a five seconds output resulting concurrently. During this time the computer does not react to any other input.

*Figure10.2*

*Printer port
sine output*

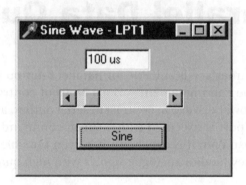

*Listing 10.1*

*AF sine
generator
program*

```
unit LPTsine;

interface

uses    PORTINC,    Windows, Messages, SysUtils, Classes,
  Graphics, Controls, Forms, Dialogs,    StdCtrls;

type
  TForm1 = class(TForm)
    ScrollBar1: TScrollBar;     Edit1: TEdit;
    Button1: TButton;
    procedure FormCreate(Sender: TObject);
    procedure Button1Click(Sender: TObject);
    procedure ScrollBar1Change(Sender: TObject);
  end;

var
  Form1: TForm1;
```

**continued on following page ...**

```
   Table : Array [0..255] of Byte;
   BA, Time: Word;

implementation

{$R *.DFM}

procedure TForm1.FormCreate(Sender: TObject);
var n: Integer;
begin
  OpenCom (Pchar('LPT1:'));
  BA := $378;
  for n := 0 to 255 do
    Table [n] := round (127.5+127.5*sin (n/128 * Pi));
  Time := 10;
end;

procedure TForm1.Button1Click(Sender: TObject);
var t: Dword;
    n: byte;
begin
  Time := ScrollBar1.Position;
  t:= 0; n:= 0;
  RealTime (true);
  TimeInitus;
  While TimeReadus < 5000000 do begin
    OutPort (BA,Table[n]);
    inc (n); t := t+Time;
    While TimeReadus < t do;
  end;
  RealTime (false);
end;

procedure TForm1.ScrollBar1Change(Sender: TObject);
begin
Edit1.Text := floattostr(Scrollbar1.Position)+' us'
end;

end.
```

## 10.2 Controlling simple machines

The printer interface has in total twelve output lines and five input lines, and with that it can control several motors and poll some switches. If single-step motors and 4-bit control are used (see Chapter 3.3), it can control three motors. This allows simple motion models to be driven, for example.

*Figure10.3*
*Connecting*
*three stepper*
*motors*

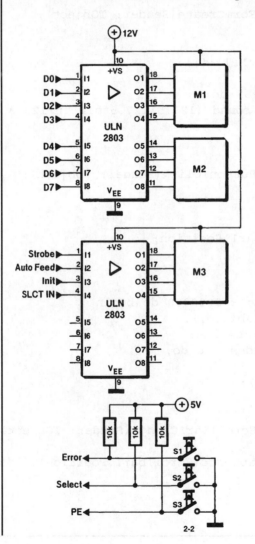

Figure10.3 shows the circuit for three stepping motors, which are driven via ULN2803 Darlington drivers. There are also three switches, which the PC can poll.

Listing 10.2 shows an example program for simple machine control. The procedures 'Motor1' to 'Motor3' generate a single step with the given rate and direction, 'left' or 'right' respectively. The three switches S1 to S3 are used as motion limiting detectors for motors M1 to M3 and are polled using the functions 'Switch1' to 'Switch3'. Accordingly, by using the procedure 'Nullposition' a definitive starting status of all motors is achieved.

The actual motion control is executed in the procedure 'Motion1', and only a very simple example is given here. All motors can be controlled singly or mutually. A brief waiting time determines the motor speed. With that at the same time the maximum speed is limited, and no step is lost. Heavily loaded motors must run more slowly.

*Figure10.4*
*Motor control*

*Listing 10.2*
*Simple control program for 3 stepper motors*

```
unit LPTMot;

interface

uses  PORTINC,Windows, Messages, SysUtils, Classes,
   Graphics, Controls, Forms, Dialogs, StdCtrls;

type
   TForm1 = class(TForm)
     Button1: TButton;  Button2: TButton;
     procedure FormCreate(Sender: TObject);
     procedure Button1Click(Sender: TObject);
     procedure Button2Click(Sender: TObject);
   end;

var
   Form1: TForm1;
   Step1, Step2, Step3 : Byte;
const BA = $378;                     { LPT1 }
      right = true;
      left = false;
```

*continued on following page ...*

# 10 Parallel Data Output

```
implementation

{$R *.DFM}

procedure Motor1 (right : Boolean);
begin
  if right then begin
    Step1 := Step1 * 2;
    if Step1 = 16 then Step1 := 1
  end else begin
    Step1 := Step1 div 2;
    if Step1 = 0 then Step1 := 8;
  end;
  OutPort(BA, Step1 + 16 * Step2);
end;

procedure Motor2 (right : Boolean);
begin
  if right then begin
    Step2 := Step2 * 2;
    if Step2 = 16 then Step2 := 1
  end else begin
    Step2 := Step2 div 2;
    if Step2 = 0 then Step2 := 8;
  end;
  OutPort(BA, Step1 + 16 * Step2);
end;

procedure Motor3 (right : Boolean);
begin
  if right then begin
    Step3 := Step3 * 2;
    if Step3 = 16 then Step3 := 1
  end else begin
    Step3 := Step3 div 2;
    if Step3 = 0 then Step3 := 8;
  end;
  OutPort(BA+2, Step3 XOR 11);
end;
```

*continued on following page . . .*

```
function Switch1: Boolean;
begin
  if (InPort(BA+1) and 8) = 0 then Switch1 := true
      else Switch1 := false;
end;
function Switch2: Boolean;
begin
  if (InPort(BA+1) and 16) = 0 then Switch2 := true
      else Switch2 := false;
end;
function Switch3: Boolean;
begin
  if (InPort(BA+1) and 32) = 0 then Switch3 := true
      else Switch3 := false;
end;

procedure NullPosition;
begin
  repeat
    Motor1(left);
    delay (5);
  until Switch1;
  repeat
    Motor2(left);
    delay (5);
  until Switch2;
  repeat
    Motor3(left);
    delay (5);
  until Switch3;
end;

procedure Motion;
var N : Word;
begin
  for n:= 1 to 100 do begin          { 100 steps }
    Motor1 (right);
    Motor2 (right);                  { all motors }
    Motor3 (right);
    delay (5);                       { fast }
  end;
```

*continued on following page . . .*

```
   for n:= 1 to 100 do begin        { 100 steps }
     Motor1 (right);                { Motor 1 only }
     delay (10);                    { slow }
   end;
   delay(1000);                     { Repose time 1 s }
   for n:= 1 to 100 do begin        { 100 steps }
     Motor1 (left);
     Motor2 (left);                 { all motors }
     Motor3 (left);
     delay(5);                      { fast }
   end;
   for n:= 1 to 100 do begin        { 100 Steps }
     Motor1 (left);                 { only Motor 1 }
     delay (10);                    { slow }
   end;
   delay (1000);                    { 1 s delay }
end;

procedure TForm1.FormCreate(Sender: TObject);
begin
   OpenCom (Pchar('LPT1:'));
   Step1 := 1;
   Step2 := 1;
   Step3 := 1;
   OutPort (BA,17);                 { D0=1, D4=1 }
   OutPort (BA+2,1 XOR 11);         { Strobe = 1 }
end;

procedure TForm1.Button1Click(Sender: TObject);
begin
   NullPosition;
end;

procedure TForm1.Button2Click(Sender: TObject);
begin
   Motion1;
end;

end.
```

# 16-bit Port Expansion

In many cases more interface port lines are needed, than those available with the printer port. In principle the number of lines may be multiplied using shift registers or register latches, but a solution with the 8243 is proposed here.

*Figure 11.1*
*8243 with*
*16 bi-directional*
*port lines*

## 11.1 The 8243 port chip

The Intel 8243 port chip offers four expansion ports each with four lines, so that a total of 16 input/output lines are available. It was actually developed for port expansion of 8048 microcontrollers, which have special instructions to support this IC. However, the 8243 is also well suited for expanding a PC interface port, since it can be controlled via a bi-directional 4-bit bus. Exactly four such lines are available on the control port of the printer interface. Figure 11.1 shows the IC pin-outs.

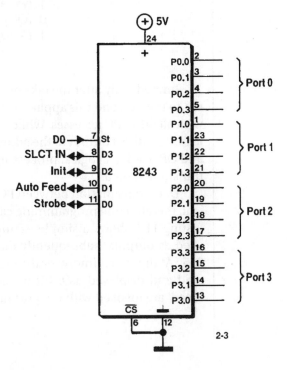

Apart from the four data lines only a single control line is needed. Data and control commands are transferred 4-bit-wise over the 8243 lines D0–D3, while a falling or rising edge of the control line St informs the 8243 whether they are control commands or data.

The control command is a 4-bit word, with a value between 0 and 15. It informs the port chip with the falling edge on the Strobe control line, which action (write, read, AND, OR) was required and which of the four expansion ports were accessed:

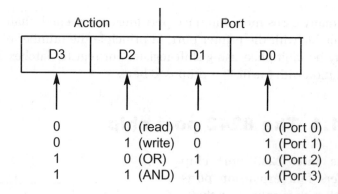

| | Action | | | | Port | |
|---|---|---|---|---|---|---|
| **D3** | | **D2** | | **D1** | | **D0** |
| 0 | | 0 (read) | | 0 | | 0 (Port 0) |
| 0 | | 1 (write) | | 0 | | 1 (Port 1) |
| 1 | | 0 (OR) | | 1 | | 0 (Port 2) |
| 1 | | 1 (AND) | | 1 | | 1 (Port 3) |

Immediately after the take over of commands the data is written to the bus, and this applies to a read access from port chip and with all other PC accesses. While a write command of a data word leads to a direct output to the addressed port, the commands AND and OR, lead to a logical processing of the old status with the new transmitted data.

Data transmission between PC and port chip is not time-critical, therefore the programming can be completed in Visual Basic. Listing 11.1 shows a simple example program. Ports 0 and 1 are used as outputs, subsequently outputting values between 0 and 255. At the same time, over the eight lines of Ports 2 and 3, data is read and displayed as 8-bit words. The subroutines 'Write' and 'Read' are invoked with the port number in the variable PORT.

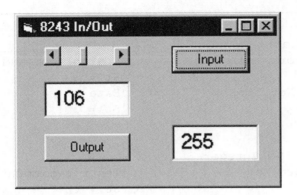

*Figure 11.2*
*Controlling*
*two 8-bit ports*

*Listing 11.1*
*8-bit input*
*and output*
*with the 8243*

```
Dim BA As Integer

Private Sub Command1_Click()
  D = HScroll1.Value
  Output 0, D Mod 16
  Output 1, D \ 16
End Sub

Private Sub Command2_Click()
  D = Input(2) + 16 * Input(3)
  Text2.Text = Str$(D)
End Sub

Private Sub Form_Load()
  If OPENCOM("LPT1:") = 0 Then MsgBox ("LPT1 not free")
  BA = &H378
  OUTPORT (BA + 2), 0                          'Output
End Sub

Private Sub Form_Unload(Cancel As Integer)
  CLOSECOM
End Sub

Private Sub HScroll1_Change()
  Text1.Text = Str$(HScroll1.Value)
End Sub
```

***continued on following page ...***

```
Sub Output(Port%, Data%)
   OUTPORT BA + 2, (Port + 4) Xor 11          'Control command
   OUTPORT BA, 0                              'St = 0
   OUTPORT BA + 2, D Xor 11                   'Data
   OUTPORT BA, 1                              'St = 1
End Sub

Function Input(Port%) As Integer
   OUTPORT BA + 2, Port Xor 11                'Control command
   OUTPORT BA, 0                              'St = 0
   OUTPORT BA + 2, 15 Xor 11                  'Bus high impedance
   Input = (INPORT(BA + 2) Xor 11) And 15 'read
   OUTPORT BA, 1                              'St = 1
End Function
```

Possible applications of this port chip are in the control of up to eight stepping motors (see Chapter 10.2) or in the checking of digital IC's (see Chapter 8.3). The 8243 can also be used as a gateway to far more complex interface circuits, when a simple computer bus is built. Besides a bi-directional 8-bit data bus (Ports 0 and 1) it is possible, for example, to define six address lines and two control lines for read and write pulses. Access to 64 I/O address locations can then be made via this bus. This is enough to build complex systems with several port chips, timers and A/D converters.

## 11.2  Expansion to 32 port lines

The 8243 contains a chip-select line, which is used to address several chips via the common 4-bit data bus. This way one can let more port chips work on a parallel interface. There are seven more lines of the 8-bit-data port free to be used as chip select lines. Figure 11.3 shows the connection of two chips, which altogether provide 32 port lines.

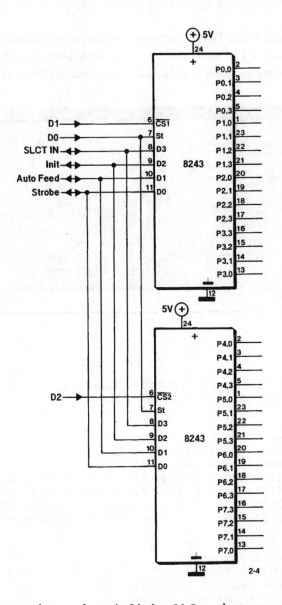

*Figure 11.3*
*Two port chips on a parallel interface*

The control procedures in Listing 11.2 work at a greater speed due to being written in Delphi. The discrete 4-bit ports of each chip are addressed in common procedures as Port 0 to Port 7. For this purpose, a corresponding chip select line is activated for Ports 0–3 and Ports 4–7.

**149**

The following Delphi program demonstrates arbitrary access to the total 32 bits on two 8243 chips, with 4-bit data transportation. By simple clicking, data can be transferred between ports.

**Figure 11.4**

*Access to 32 port lines*

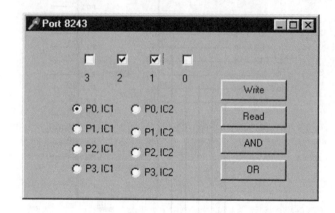

**Listing 11.2**

*Basic program - 8243 Chip data exchange*

```
unit Port8243;

interface

uses   PORTINC,Windows, Messages, SysUtils, Classes,
  Graphics, Controls, Forms, Dialogs, StdCtrls;

type
  TForm1 = class(TForm)
    CheckBox1: TCheckBox; CheckBox2: TCheckBox;
    CheckBox3: TCheckBox; CheckBox4: TCheckBox;
    RadioButton1: TRadioButton; RadioButton2: TRadioButton;
    RadioButton3: TRadioButton; RadioButton4: TRadioButton;
    RadioButton5: TRadioButton; RadioButton6: TRadioButton;
    RadioButton7: TRadioButton; RadioButton8: TRadioButton;
    Button1: TButton; Button2: TButton;
    Button3: TButton; Button4: TButton;
    Label1: TLabel; Label2: TLabel;
    Label3: TLabel; Label4: TLabel;
    procedure FormCreate(Sender: TObject);
    procedure Button1Click(Sender: TObject);
    procedure Button2Click(Sender: TObject);
    procedure Button3Click(Sender: TObject);
    procedure Button4Click(Sender: TObject);
  end;
```

*continued on following page . . .*

```
var
  Form1: TForm1;
const BA = $378;                                  { LPT1 }

implementation

{$R *.DFM}

procedure Set (Port_Nr,Value: Byte);
var CS : Byte;
begin
  If (Port_Nr div 4)=0 then CS := 4;              { D1=CS1=0 }
  If (Port_Nr div 4)=1 then CS := 2;              { D2=CS2=0 }
  OutPort (BA, CS + 1);                           { D0=St=1 }
  OutPort (BA+2,((Port_Nr AND 3) + 4) XOR 11); { Control com}
  OutPort (BA, CS);                               { D0=St=0 }
  OutPort (BA+2, Value XOR 11);                   { Data word }
  OutPort (BA, CS + 1);                           { D0=St=1 }
  OutPort (BA, 6 + 1);                            { CS1=1, CS2=1}
end;

function Read (Port_Nr : Byte): Byte;
var CS : Byte;
begin
  If (Port_Nr div 4)=0 then CS := 4;              { D1=CS1=0 }
  If (Port_Nr div 4)=1 then CS := 2;              { D2=CS2=0 }
  OutPort (BA, CS + 1);                           { D0=St=1 }
  OutPort (BA+2,(Port_Nr AND 3) XOR 11);          { Control command}
  OutPort (BA, CS);                               { D0=St=0 }
  OutPort (BA+2, 15 XOR 11);                      { Bus high ohm.}
  Read := InPort(BA+2) AND 15 XOR 11;             { Data read }
  OutPort (BA, CS + 1);                           { D0=St=1 }
  OutPort (BA, 6 + 1);                            { CS1=1, CS2=1}
end;

procedure AND_Port (Port_Nr,Value: Byte); var CS : Byte;
begin
  If (Port_Nr div 4)=0 then CS := 4;              { D1=CS1=0 }
  If (Port_Nr div 4)=1 then CS := 2;              { D2=CS2=0 }
  OutPort (BA, CS + 1);                           { D0=St=1 }
  OutPort (BA+2,((Port_Nr AND 3) + 12) XOR 11); { Control
        command}
  OutPort (BA, CS);                               { D0=St=0 }
  OutPort (BA+2, Value XOR 11);                   { Data word }
  OutPort (BA, CS + 1);                           { D0=St=1 }
  OutPort (BA, 6 + 1);                            { CS1=1, CS2=1}
end;
```

*continued on following page ...*

```
procedure OR_PORT (Port_Nr,Value: Byte);
var CS : Byte;
begin
  If (Port_Nr div 4)=0 then CS := 4;        { D1=CS1=0 }
  If (Port_Nr div 4)=1 then CS := 2;        { D2=CS2=0 }
  OutPort (BA, CS + 1);                      { D0=St=1 }
  OutPort (BA+2,((Port_Nr AND 3) + 8) XOR 11);  { Control
      command}
  OutPort (BA, CS);                          { D0=St=0 }
  OutPort (BA+2, Value XOR 11);              { Data word }
  OutPort (BA, CS + 1);                      { D0=St=1 }
  OutPort (BA, 6 + 1);                       { CS1=1, CS2=1}
end;

Function Value: Byte;
var Read: Byte;
begin
  Read := 0;
  if Form1.CheckBox1.Checked then Read := Read + 1;
  if Form1.CheckBox2.Checked then Read := Read + 2;
  if Form1.CheckBox3.Checked then Read := Read + 4;
  if Form1.CheckBox4.Checked then Read := Read + 8;
  Value := Read;
end;

Function Port_Nr: Byte;
begin
  if Form1.RadioButton1.Checked Then Port_Nr := 0;
  if Form1.RadioButton2.Checked Then Port_Nr := 1;
  if Form1.RadioButton3.Checked Then Port_Nr := 2;
  if Form1.RadioButton4.Checked Then Port_Nr := 3;
end;

procedure TForm1.FormCreate(Sender: TObject);
begin
  OpenCom (Pchar('LPT1:'));
end;

procedure TForm1.Button1Click(Sender: TObject);
begin
  Set (Port_Nr,Value);
end;
```

*continued on following page ...*

```
procedure TForm1.Button2Click(Sender: TObject);
var Result: Byte;
begin
  Result :=Read (Port_Nr);
  CheckBox1.Checked := ((Result And 1) = 1);
  CheckBox2.Checked := ((Result And 2) = 2);
  CheckBox3.Checked := ((Result And 4) = 4);
  CheckBox4.Checked := ((Result And 8) = 8);
end;

procedure TForm1.Button3Click(Sender: TObject);
begin
  AND_Port (Port_Nr, Value);
end;

procedure TForm1.Button4Click(Sender: TObject);
begin
  OR_Port (Port_Nr, Value);
end;

end.
```

## 11.3 EPROM programmer

EPROM's are electrically programmable data storage IC's that can be erased using ultraviolet light. They are used for control programs in small computer systems, computer operating systems, control data for complex circuits and many other applications. There is often a need to read data from an EPROM, to copy the contents or to program an EPROM with existing data. For interim data storage, files on diskettes are used. These can be regarded as simple EPROM copies, and for example come in the form of a list of bytes, which is also called a binary file. To copy an EPROM, it is first read and its contents are copied to file such as 'DATA.BIN'. Then a new or erased EPROM is programmed with this data.

An EPROM contains a large number of memory locations, and each set of eight memory locations forms a single data byte. Which of the memory cells are connected to the eight data lines at any given time is determined by the status of the address lines. In order to put EPROM data on the data lines, control signals must also be provided. For programming, in addition to the normal supply voltage of 5 V, a higher programming voltage must be provided, for example 12.5 V. Data must be applied to the data lines and then a brief programming pulse 'burns' the data into the addressed memory area.

The EPROM programmer introduced here is suitable for reading and programming EPROM types 2764, 27128 and 27256. Besides eight data lines, up to 15 address lines and a control signal must be provided. The device needs two 8243 port chips, where ports 0 and 1 are combined to form a bi-directional data bus and ports 2 to 5 are used as the address bus together. Figure 11.5 shows the diagram of the 32-bit expansion port from Section 11.2.

*Figure 11.5*
*EPROM*
*programmer*
*for connection*
*to two 8243*
*port chips*

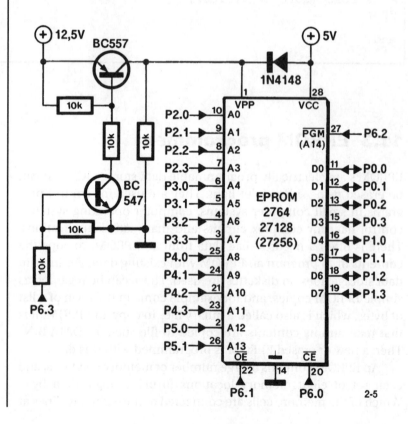

Port 6 provides the necessary control lines. /CS is used to activate the EPROM. /OE activates the data direction 'read' when low. Vpp is the terminal for the programming voltage. Newer EPROMs mostly need 12.5 V, older ones must be still programmed with 21 V.

For the 2764 and 27128, pin 23 of the EPROM has the function PGM, for the activation of programming events. The 27256 does without this control line in favour of address line A14.

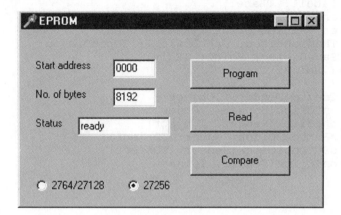

*Figure 11.6*
*Programming*
*display*

The control program in Listing 10.3 can be used for all three EPROM types. Through clicking of the related button, programming of the 27256 is possible. Thereto the control line PGM is then used as the address line A14.

The program can read EPROMs and transfer their contents in binary format. After the burning of binary data into the EPROM an additional comparison of data is performed. With burning, faster programming algorithms are used: each byte is often repeatedly burnt with a programming time of circa one millisecond until the correct content is read back. Then follows a three times longer programming to ensure long term data stability. In contrast to old procedures, which fundamentally worked with 50 ms, it provides a considerable time saving.

*Listing 11.3  EPROM programmer for up to 32 KB*

```pascal
unit Eprom;

interface

uses   PORTINC,Windows, Messages, SysUtils, Classes,
   Graphics, Controls, Forms, Dialogs, StdCtrls;

type
  TForm1 = class(TForm)
    Edit1: TEdit; Label1: TLabel;
    Button1: TButton; Button2: TButton;
    Button3: TButton; RadioButton1: TRadioButton;
    RadioButton2: TRadioButton; OpenDialog1: TOpenDialog;
    SaveDialog1: TSaveDialog; Edit2: TEdit;
    Label2: TLabel; Edit3: TEdit;
    Label3: TLabel;
    procedure FormCreate(Sender: TObject);
    procedure Button1Click(Sender: TObject);
    procedure Button2Click(Sender: TObject);
    procedure RadioButton2Click(Sender: TObject);
    procedure RadioButton1Click(Sender: TObject);
    procedure Button3Click(Sender: TObject);
  end;

var
  Form1: TForm1;
  Typ256: Boolean;
  Address, Count: Integer;
const BA = $378;                                    { LPT1 }

implementation

{$R *.DFM}

procedure Set (Port_Nr,Value: Byte);
var CS : Byte;
begin
  If (Port_Nr div 4)=0 then CS := 4;        { D1=CS1=0 }
  If (Port_Nr div 4)=1 then CS := 2;        { D2=CS2=0 }
  OutPort (BA, CS + 1);                      { D0=St=1 }
  OutPort (BA+2,(Port_Nr AND 3)+4) XOR 11);  { Control command}
  OutPort (BA, CS);                          { D0=St=0 }
  OutPort (BA+2, Value XOR 11);              { Data word }
  OutPort (BA, CS + 1);                      { D0=St=1 }
  OutPort (BA, 6 + 1);                       { CS1=1, CS2=1}
end;
```

**continued on following page . . .**

```
function Read (Port_Nr : Byte): Byte;
var CS : Byte;
begin
  If (Port_Nr div 4)=0 then CS := 4;          { D1=CS1=0 }
  If (Port_Nr div 4)=1 then CS := 2;          { D2=CS2=0 }
  OutPort (BA, CS + 1);                        { D0=St=1 }
  OutPort (BA+2,(Port_Nr AND 3) XOR 11);       { Control command}
  OutPort (BA, CS);                            { D0=St=0 }
  OutPort (BA+2, 15 XOR 11);                   { Bus high ohm.}
  Delayus (10);
  Read := InPort(BA+2) AND 15 XOR 11;          { Data read }
  OutPort (BA, CS + 1);                        { D0=St=1 }
  OutPort (BA, 6 + 1);                         { CS1=1, CS2=1}
end;

procedure AND_Port (Port_Nr,Value: Byte); var CS : Byte;
begin
  If (Port_Nr div 4)=0 then CS := 4;          { D1=CS1=0 }
  If (Port_Nr div 4)=1 then CS := 2;          { D2=CS2=0 }
  OutPort (BA, CS + 1);                        { D0=St=1 }
  OutPort (BA+2,((Port_Nr AND 3)+12) XOR 11); { Control cmd}
  OutPort (BA, CS);                            { D0=St=0 }
  OutPort (BA+2, Value XOR 11);                { Data word }
  OutPort (BA, CS + 1);                        { D0=St=1 }
  OutPort (BA, 6 + 1);                         { CS1=1, CS2=1}
end;

procedure OR_PORT (Port_Nr,Value: Byte);
var CS : Byte;
begin
  If (Port_Nr div 4)=0 then CS := 4;          { D1=CS1=0 }
  If (Port_Nr div 4)=1 then CS := 2;          { D2=CS2=0 }
  OutPort (BA, CS + 1);                        { D0=St=1 }
  OutPort (BA+2,((Port_Nr AND 3)+8) XOR 11);  { Control command}
  OutPort (BA, CS);                            { D0=St=0 }
  OutPort (BA+2, Value XOR 11);                { Data word }
  OutPort (BA, CS + 1);                        { D0=St=1 }
  OutPort (BA, 6 + 1);                         { CS1=1, CS2=1}
end;

procedure DataSet (Value: Byte);
begin
  Set (0, Value mod 16);                       { P0: D0..D3 }
  Set (1, Value div 16);                       { P1: D4..D7 }
end;
```

*continued on following page ...*

```
function DataRead: Byte;
begin
  DataRead := Read (0) + 16 * Read (1);     { twice }
  DataRead := Read (0) + 16 * Read (1);     { P0,P1 read}
end;

procedure AddressSet (Address: Word); begin
  Set (2, Lo (Address) mod 16);             { P2: A0...A3 }
  Set (3, Lo (Address) div 16);             { P3: A4...A7 }
  Set (4, Hi (Address) mod 16);             { P4: A8...A11 }
  Set (5, Hi (Address) div 16);             { P5: A12...A13}
  If Typ256 then begin
    if Address < 16384 then AND_Port (6,11) { P62=A14=0 }
    else OR_Port (6,4);                     { P62=A14=1 }
  end;
end;

function Outread (Address: Word): Byte; begin
  Set (6,4);                                {/CE=0, /OE=0 }
  AddressSet (Address);
  Outread := Dataread;
end;

procedure Burn (Address: Word; Value: Byte); begin
  AddressSet (Address);
  DataSet (Value);
  If Typ256 then begin
    OR_Port (6,11);                         { /OE=1, Vpp on}
    AND_Port (6,14);                        { /CE=0 }
  end else Set (6,10);                      { Vpp, /OE=1,
     /PGM=0 }
  delay (1);                                { 1 ms burn }
  Set (6,7);                         { Upp out, /CE=1, /PGM=1}
end;

procedure BurnandCheck (Address: Word; Value: Byte);
var n, m: Integer;
begin
  n := 0;
  repeat
    Burn (Address,Value);
    n := n + 1;                             { n * 1 ms }
  until (Value >= Outread (Address)) or (n=50);
  for m := 1 to 3*n do Burn (Address,Value);    {3*n ms}
end;
```

*continued on following page ...*

```
procedure TForm1.FormCreate(Sender: TObject);
begin
   OpenCom (Pchar('LPT1:'));
   Typ256 := True;
end;

procedure TForm1.Button1Click(Sender: TObject);
 VAR  f :file of byte;
      r,value :Byte;
      Address, n, Code : Integer;
begin
   val (Edit1.Text, Address, Code);
   OpenDialog1.FileName := '*.bin';
   OpenDiaLog1.Execute;
   if OpenDialog1.FileName > '' then begin
     AssignFile(f,OpenDialog1.Filename);
     {$I-} Reset(f); {$I+}
     r:=IOResult;
     IF r = 0 then begin
       for n:= 1 to filesize (f) do begin
          Read(f,value);
          BurnandCheck (Address+n-1,Value);
       end;
       CloseFile(f);
       Edit3.Text := 'Burn OK'
     end;
   end;
end;

procedure TForm1.Button2Click(Sender: TObject);
 VAR  f :file of byte;
      r,value :Byte;
      Address, Count,n, Code : Integer;
begin
   val (Edit1.Text, Address, Code);
   val (Edit2.Text, Count, Code);
   SaveDialog1.FileName := '*.bin';
   SaveDiaLog1.Execute;
   if SaveDialog1.FileName > '' then begin
     AssignFile(f,SaveDialog1.Filename);
     {$I-} Rewrite(f); {$I+}
     r:=IOResult;
     IF r = 0 then begin
       for n:= Address to (Address+Count-1) do begin
          Value := Outread (n);
          write (f,Value);
       end;
```

*continued on following page . . .*

```
        CloseFile(f);
        end;
        Edit3.Text := 'OK';
   end;
end;

procedure TForm1.RadioButton2Click(Sender: TObject);
begin
   Typ256 := false;
end;

procedure TForm1.RadioButton1Click(Sender: TObject);
begin
   Typ256 := true;
end;

procedure TForm1.Button3Click(Sender: TObject);
 VAR  f :file of byte;
      r,value :Byte;
      Address, Count,n, Code : Integer;
      Error : Boolean;
begin
   Error := false;
   val (Edit1.Text, Address, Code);
   OpenDialog1.FileName := '*.bin';
   OpenDiaLog1.Execute;
   if OpenDialog1.FileName > '' then begin
     AssignFile(f,OpenDialog1.Filename);
     {$I-} Reset(f); {$I+}
     r:=IOResult;
     IF r = 0 then begin
        for n:= 1 to filesize (f) do begin
          Read(f,value);
          If Value <> Outread (Address+n-1) then Error := true;
        end;
        CloseFile(f);
     end;
        if Error then Edit3.Text := 'Error!'
           else Edit3.Text := 'EPROM OK';
   end;
end;

end.
```

# The I$^2$C Bus

The I$^2$C bus (Inter-IC bus) is a 2-wire data link between one or more master processors and several slave peripheral chips. All chips reside on the same bus and are designed to communicate at their respective addresses. Addresses and data are both transmitted over the same lines. The bus permits a very simple connection between many IC's and provides trouble-free expansion.

All IC's using the I$^2$C bus protocol can be connected. As well as RAMs, EEPROMs, port expansion chips, A/D and D/A converters and clock chips, there are many special IC's, such as display drivers and IC's for TV applications. All these chips provide direct trouble-free control over two lines of the PC parallel interface. With a few additional devices the serial interface can also be used.

## 12.1 Data transmission and addressing

The I$^2$C bus uses the serial data line SDA and the clock line SCL. Both data and addresses are transferred in the same way as with shift registers, together with a clock signal. Both lines are used in each data direction. They are both supplied with a pull-up resistor and can be pulled down by each bus device through open collector or open drain outputs in an FET. Inactive bus devices are at high impedance, but continue monitoring the bus signal. When only one master is required, this master alone outputs the clock signal. The data can however come from the slave as well as from the master.

*Figure 12.1*
*I²C bus*
*connections*
*between master*
*and slave IC's*

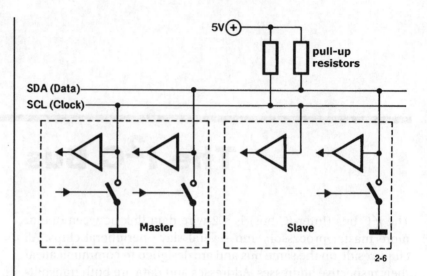

The I²C bus protocol accurately defines a series of specific situations, which each bus participant is permitted to recognise; start and end of a transmission; as well as recognising its own address:

- *quiescent state:* SDA and SCL are high and inactive
- *Start condition:* SDA is pulled down by the master, while SCL stays high
- *Stop condition:* SDA changes from low to high, while SCL stays high
- *data transmission:* The actual sender outputs eight data bits to the SDA data line, which are shifted by the master through clock pulses on the clock line SCL. The transmission begins with the most significant bit.
- *Acknowledge:* The receiver acknowledges receipt of a byte by outputting a low level on SDA, until the master has generated the ninth clock pulse on SCL. The confirmation means at the same time, that a further byte will be receipted. A known end of transmission must be announced by the absence of confirmation acknowledge. Actual transmission end is achieved through the Stop condition.

Addresses are transmitted and acknowledged in the same way as data transmissions. In the simplest case of a data transmission from master to a slave, for example an output port, the following events take place: the master generates the start condition and then in bits 7–1, transfers the address of the port chip, and in bit 0 the required data transmission direction, namely 0 for 'Write'. The slave acknowledges the address. The master sends the data byte, which is likewise acknowledged. It can now stop the connection with the stop condition or send further bytes to the same slave.

$I^2C$ bus address with data direction bit

| A6 | A5 | A4 | A3 | A2 | A1 | A0 | R/W |
|----|----|----|----|----|----|----|-----|

If data is to be read from a slave, the address must be transferred with the data direction bit set high. The master outputs eight clock pulses and receives eight data bits. As long as it acknowledges receipt with the ninth clock pulse, it can receive further Bytes. The transmission is eventually terminated by the master through an absence confirmation and the stop condition.

Each $I^2C$ chip has a defined address, which is partly determined by the chip specification and to another part can be changed by address lines on the chip terminals. This means, that for example with three address lines, up to eight chips of same type can be connected to the bus.

The maximum clock rate for the $I^2C$ bus is 100kHz. In the following program, waiting times from 10 μs are used in order to avoid exceeding the maximum speed with faster computers.

## 12.2  Control via the parallel interface

The connection from $I^2C$ bus ICs to the parallel interface turns out to be very simple, because the bi-directional lines Strobe and Auto Feed can be directly used as SDA and SCL. The required pull up resistors are already contained in the PC. Figure 12.2 shows the

*Figure 12.2*
*I²C bus chip*
*connections*
*to the parallel*
*interface*

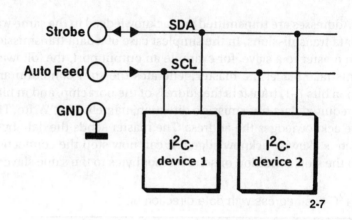

principal connection. The basic software with the necessary transmission routine was introduced as the unit 'I2CLPT1' for the first parallel interface in Listing 12.1. It must be borne in mind, that both signal lines in the PC are inverted, and each bit must be inverted by the software.

*Listing 12.1*

*Unit for*
*controlling the*
*I²C bus via*
*the parallel*
*interface*

All procedures, in which clock pulses are generated, are delayed with Delayus(10), in order not to run the bus too fast. The unit already opens the interface and initialises the lines SDA and SCL. At the highest level of the application programs, the programmer can query the successful communication with an IC , as the function Output evaluates the acknowledge signal and returns the success. In the event of an error, or for example, an invalid IC address being used, 'false' is returned.

```
unit I2CLPT1;

interface

uses   PORTINC, Windows;

const BA = $378;

Procedure I2C_Init;
Procedure Start;
```

*continued on following page ...*

```
Procedure Stop;
Procedure Acknowledge;
Procedure NoAcknowledge;
Function Output (Value : Byte): Boolean;
Function  Inread : Byte;

implementation

procedure I2C_Init;
begin
  OpenCOM (Pchar('LPT1:'));
  OutPort (BA+2,0);                         { SCL=1, SDA=1 }
end;

procedure Start;
begin
  OutPort (BA+2,1);                         { SDA=0 }
  OutPort (BA+2,3);                         { SCL=0 }
end;

procedure Stop;
begin
  OutPort (BA+2,3);                         { SCL=0, SDA=0 }
  OutPort (BA+2,1);                         { SCL=1 }
  OutPort (BA+2,0);                         { SDA=1 }
end;

procedure Acknowledge;
begin
  OutPort (BA+2,3);                         { SCL=0, SDA=0 }
  OutPort (BA+2,1);                         { SCL=1 }
  Delayus (10);                             { Waiting time }
  OutPort (BA+2,3);                         { SCL=0 }
end;

procedure NoAcknowledge;
begin
  OutPort (BA+2,2);                         { SCL=0, SDA=1 }
  OutPort (BA+2,0);                         { SCL=1 }
  Delayus (10);                             { Waiting time }
  OutPort (BA+2,2);                         { SCL=0 }
end;
```

*continued on following page ...*

```
Function Output (Value : Byte): Boolean;
var Bitvalue, Portvalue, n : Byte;
begin
  Output := true;
  Bitvalue := 128;
  for n:= 1 to 8 do begin
    if (Value AND Bitvalue) = Bitvalue then Portvalue := 2
      else Portvalue := 3;
    OutPort (BA+2,Portvalue);              { SDA set }
    OutPort (BA+2,Portvalue-2);            { SCL=1 }
    Delayus (10);                          { Waiting time }
    OutPort (BA+2,Portvalue);              { SCL=0 }
    Bitvalue := Bitvalue div 2;
  end;
  OutPort (BA+2,2);                        { SDA=1, SCL=0 }
  OutPort (BA+2,0);                        { SCL=1, SDA read }
  Delayus (10);                           { Waiting time }
  if (InPort(BA+2) AND 1) = 0 then
    Output := False;
  OutPort (BA+2,2);                        { SCL=0 }
end;

function Inread : Byte;
var Bitvalue, Value, n : Byte;
begin
  OutPort (BA+2,2);                        { SDA=1, SCL=0 }
  Bitvalue := 128;
  Value := 0;
  for n:= 1 to 8 do begin
    OutPort (BA+2,0);                      { SCL=1, SDA read }
    Delayus (10);                          { Waiting time }
    If (InPort (BA+2) AND 1) = 0 then
        Value := Value + Bitvalue;
    OutPort (BA+2,2);                      { SCL=0 }
    Bitvalue := Bitvalue div 2;
  end;
  Inread := Value;
end;

end.
```

## 12.3  Serial interface connection

Making a connection to the I$^2$C bus via the serial interface is requires slightly more effort, but it also offers certain advantages, particularly regarding the safety of the PC. Furthermore, several serial interfaces are often present, whereas the printer usually occupies the parallel interface.

As there are no bi-directional lines on the serial interface, inputs and outputs must be combined. Figure 12.3 shows the connections. In the quiescent state DTR and RTS output a high level, which is limited to permitted voltage limits using Zener diodes. The usual open-collector output is redundant, when instead of this, the lines are directly switched for outputting low levels. Reading back status is only necessary for the SDA line, as long as no second master is planned.

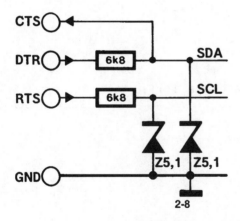

*Figure 12.3*
*I$^2$C bus on the serial interface*

The basic software, as shown in Listing 12.2, uses COM2 and differs very little from the software for the parallel interface . All equivalent procedures and functions have the same names. Thanks to the unit concept, existing programs can be used without large additional effort equally well for the parallel and serial interfaces.

**Listing 12.2**

*Basic basic software for the I²C serial interface*

An essential advantage of unit 'I2CCOM2' is evident, i.e. no direct port instructions are used, only DTR(), RTS() et al. The concept is therefore equally valid under Windows NT as these functions only use permitted access via. Windows drivers.

```
unit I2CCOM2;

interface

uses  PORTINC, Windows;

Procedure I2C_Init;
Procedure Start;
Procedure Stop;
Procedure Acknowledge;
Procedure NoAcknowledge;
Function Output (Value : Byte): Boolean;
Function  Inread : Byte;

implementation

procedure I2C_Init;
begin
  OpenCom (Pchar('com2:9600,N,8,1'));
  RTS(1); DTR(1);                          { SCL=1, SDA=1 }
end;

procedure Start;
begin
  DTR(0);                                  { SDA=0 }
  RTS(0);                                  { SCL=0 }
end;

procedure Stop;
begin
  RTS(0); DTR(0);                          { SCL=0, SDA=0 }
  RTS(1);                                  { SCL=1 }
  DTR(1);                                  { SDA=1 }
end;
```

***continued on following page ...***

```
procedure Acknowledge;
begin
  RTS(0); DTR(0);                            { SCL=0, SDA=0 }
  RTS(1);                                    { SCL=1 }
  Delayus (10);                              { Wait loop }
  RTS(0);                                    { SCL=0 }
end;

procedure NoAcknowledge;
begin
  RTS(0); DTR(1);                            { SCL=0, SDA=1 }
  RTS(1);                                    { SCL=1 }
  Delayus (10);                              { Wait loop }
  RTS(0);                                    { SCL=0 }
end;

Function Output (Value : Byte): Boolean;
var Bitvalue, n: Byte;
begin
  Output := true;
  Bitvalue := 128;
  for n:= 1 to 8 do begin
    if (Value AND Bitvalue) = Bitvalue then DTR(1)
     else DTR(0);                            { SDA set }
    RTS(1);                                  { SCL=1 }
    Delayus (10);                            { Wait loop }
    RTS(0);                                  { SCL=0 }
    Bitvalue := Bitvalue div 2;
  end;
  DTR(1);                                    { SDA=1 }
  RTS(1);                                    { SCL=1, SDA read }
  Delayus (10);                              { Wait loop }
  if CTS = 1 then Output := False;
  RTS(0);                                    { SCL=0 }
end;

function Inread : Byte;
var Bitvalue, Value, n: Byte;
begin
  RTS(0); DTR(1);                            { SDA=1, SCL=0 }
  Bitvalue := 128;
  Value := 0;
```

*continued on following page ...*

**169**

```
for n:= 1 to 8 do begin
   RTS(1);                                    { SCL=1, SDA read }
   Delayus (10);                              { Wait loop }
   If CTS = 1 then Value := Value + Bitvalue;
   RTS(0);                                    { SCL=0 }
   Bitvalue := Bitvalue div 2;
 end;
 Inread := Value;
end;

end.
```

## 12.4 PCF8574 port expansion chip

Port chips for the I2C bus have the advantage of a simple connection and are easily expandable. The Philips PCF8574 provides eight port lines, which can be used for read and write. Figure 12.4 shows the pin assignments. The SDA and SCL lines are decoupled using 330-Ω resistors, in order to damp any transitory pulses on long lines. Three address lines are available here and can be used to address up to eight chips of the same kind. The type-specific base address is 32. A supplementary open-drain interrupt output reports all changes on the input lines by means of a LOW level. This interrupt is reset by any read access.

*Figure 12.4*
*PCF8574
port chip pin
assignments*

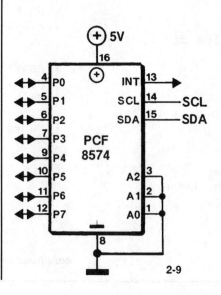

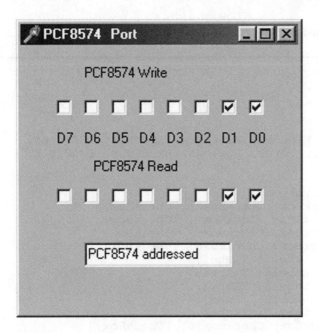

*Figure 12.5*
*PCF8574*
*chip access*

Special switching of the data direction as with the 8243 is not necessary, since the PCF8574 uses bi-directional lines. In the quiescent state, the discrete port lines are high and are at high impedance, so that they can be pulled down by external circuitry. With any output of a low level, lines are pulled down actively and at low impedance. The port can also be used partly for input and partly for output. Read lines must only be set high first by an output command.

Listing 12.3 shows a simple program for direct communication with the port chip. By clicking, the user can determine which lines are set high. The status of the lines is read back at the same time. Lines that were set high by the user can be pulled down externally. At the same time, the program reports the actual connection status, so that errors can be recognised.

The program uses access via the COM2 serial interface; however, it can also be used for the parallel interface by replacing the unit that is used (I2CLPT1).

*Listing 12.3* Direct data transmission from PC to PCF8574

```
unit PCF8574;

interface

uses
   I2CCOM2, PORTINC, Windows, Messages, SysUtils, Classes,
   Graphics, Controls, Forms, Dialogs, ExtCtrls, StdCtrls;

type
   TForm1 = class(TForm)
      CheckBox1: TCheckBox; CheckBox2: TCheckBox;
      CheckBox3: TCheckBox; CheckBox4: TCheckBox;
      CheckBox5: TCheckBox; CheckBox6: TCheckBox;
      CheckBox7: TCheckBox; CheckBox8: TCheckBox;
      Label1: TLabel; Label2: TLabel;
      Label3: TLabel; Label4: TLabel;
      Label5: TLabel; Label6: TLabel;
      Label7: TLabel; Label8: TLabel;
      Timer1: TTimer; Label9: TLabel;
      CheckBox9: TCheckBox; CheckBox10: TCheckBox;
      CheckBox11: TCheckBox; CheckBox12: TCheckBox;
      CheckBox13: TCheckBox; CheckBox14: TCheckBox;
      CheckBox15: TCheckBox; CheckBox16: TCheckBox;
      Label10: TLabel; Edit1: TEdit;
      procedure FormCreate(Sender: TObject);
      procedure Timer1Timer(Sender: TObject);
   end;

var
   Form1: TForm1;
   Dout, Din, Ain: Byte;
   Error: Boolean;

implementation

{$R *.DFM}

Procedure ParallelOut (Value: Byte);
begin
   Start;
   Error:=Not(Output (32 * 2));  {Adr 32, Ack?}
   Output (Value);
   Stop;
end;
```

*continued on following page . . .*

```
function ParallelIn : Byte;
begin
  Start;
  Error:=Not(Output (32 * 2 + 1)); {Adr 32, read}
  ParallelIn := Inread;
  NoAcknowledge;
  Stop;
end;

procedure TForm1.FormCreate(Sender: TObject);
begin
  I2C_Init;
  Timer1.Interval := 100;
  Timer1.Enabled := true;
end;

procedure TForm1.Timer1Timer(Sender: TObject);
begin
  Dout := 0;
  if  CheckBox1.Checked Then Dout := Dout +1;
  if  CheckBox2.Checked Then Dout := Dout +2;
  if  CheckBox3.Checked Then Dout := Dout +4;
  if  CheckBox4.Checked Then Dout := Dout +8;
  if  CheckBox5.Checked Then Dout := Dout +16;
  if  CheckBox6.Checked Then Dout := Dout +32;
  if  CheckBox7.Checked Then Dout := Dout +64;
  if  CheckBox8.Checked Then Dout := Dout +128;
  ParallelOut (Dout);
  If Error Then Edit1.Text := 'IC not responding'
    else Edit1.Text := 'PCF8574 addressed';
  Din := ParallelIn;
  CheckBox9.Checked  := ((Din And 1) >0);
  CheckBox10.Checked := ((Din And 2) >0);
  CheckBox11.Checked := ((Din And 4) >0);
  CheckBox12.Checked := ((Din And 8) >0);
  CheckBox13.Checked := ((Din And 16) >0);
  CheckBox14.Checked := ((Din And 32) >0);
  CheckBox15.Checked := ((Din And 64) >0);
  CheckBox16.Checked := ((Din And 128) >0);
 end;

end.
```

**Figure 12.6**

*Logic analyser
using the
PCF8574*

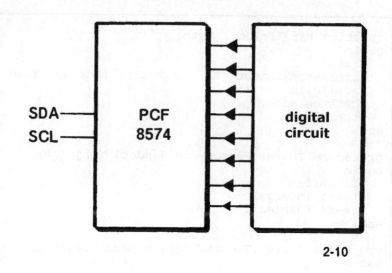

When port expanders are either only to be written or read, repeated transmission of the address is to be avoided, so that greater transmission speeds can be achieved. Figure 12.6 shows the PCF8574 in an application as a logic analyser. With that the status of eight digital lines are monitored in faster sequence. This is for example helpful, with the error search in digital circuitry.

Listing 12.4 shows control of the chip as a logic analyser. Whereas in procedures 'Parallelin' and 'ParallelOut', data bytes are only transmitted at one time, the procedure 'Series' demonstrates repeated port reads without renewed addressing.

The address must first be transmitted after every start condition, followed by the data byte. With the read, each byte except the last must be confirmed through Acknowledge. The chip connection is terminated with the stop condition.

The program uses all PCF8574 port lines as inputs. Their status is queried in a fast loop and stored in a data buffer. Figure 12.7 shows a screen dump of the plot.

*Listing 12.4* PCF8574 application - logic analyser

```
unit Logic;

interface

uses I2CCOM2,PORTINC, Windows, Messages, SysUtils, Classes,
Graphics, Controls, Forms, Dialogs, StdCtrls, ExtCtrls;

type
  TForm1 = class(TForm)
    PaintBox1: TPaintBox;
    Start: TButton;
    procedure FormCreate(Sender: TObject);
    procedure StartClick(Sender: TObject);
  end;

var
  Form1: TForm1;
  Buffer : Array [1..5000] of Byte;

implementation

{$R *.DFM}

procedure ParallelOut (Value: Byte);
begin
  Start;
  Output (32 * 2);                           { Address 32, write }
  Output (Value);
  Stop;
end;

function ParallelIn : Byte;
begin
  Start;
  Output (32 * 2 + 1);                        { Address 32, read }
  ParallelIn := Inread;
  NoAcknowledge;
  Stop;
end;

procedure Series;
var Dummy : Byte;
    m, n: Word;
```

***continued on following page ...***

```
begin
   ParallelOut (255);
   Start;
   Output (32 * 2 + 1);                  { Address 32, read }
   for n := 1 to 400 do begin;
       Buffer [n] := Inread;             { 400 times Data read }
       Acknowledge;                      { Receive confirmation }
       delay (10);
   end;
   Dummy := Inread;                      { once inread }
   NoAcknowledge;                        { not confirmed }
   Stop;                                 { disconnected }
end;

procedure TForm1.FormCreate(Sender: TObject);
begin
   I2C_Init;
   Paintbox1.Canvas.Pen.Color:=ClBlack;
   Paintbox1.Canvas.Brush.Color:=ClWhite;
   PaintBox1.Canvas.Rectangle(0,0,400,160);
end;

procedure TForm1.StartClick(Sender: TObject);
var n, m, Value: Integer;
begin
   Series;
   Paintbox1.Canvas.Pen.Color:=ClLtGray;
   Paintbox1.Canvas.Brush.Color:=ClWhite;
   PaintBox1.Canvas.Rectangle(0,0,401,161);
   for n:= 1 to 8 do begin
       paintbox1.canvas.MoveTo(0,n*20);
       Paintbox1.Canvas.Lineto (400,n*20);
   end;
   Paintbox1.Canvas.Pen.Color:=ClBlack;
   Value := 1;
   for n := 1 to 8 do begin
     for m := 2 to 400 do begin
       paintbox1.canvas.MoveTo (m-1,
             n*20-12*((Buffer[m-1] and Value) div Value));
       Paintbox1.Canvas.Lineto   (m,
             n*20-12*((Buffer[m] and Value) div Value));
     end;
     Value := Value * 2;
   end;
end;

end.
```

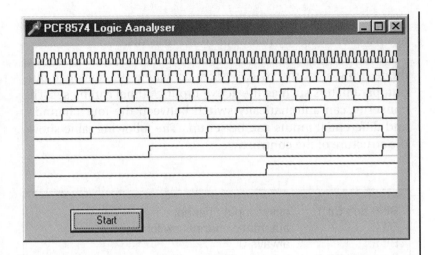

*Figure 12.7*

*Screen display
of the status
of eight
digital lines*

## 12.5 PCF8591 A/D and D/A converter

The Philips PCF8591
$I^2C$ bus chip has four
analogue input chan-
nels and one analogue
output channel. The
resolution is eight bits
respectively circa 20mV
with the highest refer-
ence voltage of 5 V. The
base address is 72, but
up to eight converters
can be addressed using
three externally accessi-
ble address lines. Figure
12.8 shows how the chip
is connected, with the
SDA and SCL lines again
being decoupled by
330-Ω resistors.

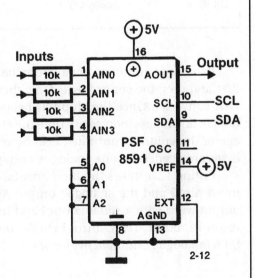

*Figure 12.8*

*Connecting the
PCF8591
A/D and D/A
converter*

The analogue inputs of the converter should be protected against overvoltage by means of 10-kΩ resistors.

The PCF8591 must be configured to the required operating mode using a control byte. Besides activating the analogue output, parameters such as the active input channel can be set. The converter can automatically switch between the four channels, and differential inputs can be set up. The following table shows the structure of the control byte.

| | |
|---|---|
| Bit 0 and Bit 1: | active input channel |
| Bit 2: | automatic channel switching |
| Bit 3: | always 0 |
| Bit 4 and Bit 5: | input configuration: |
| | 00: all channels tied to ground |
| | 01: three differential input referred to Ain 3 |
| | 10: Ain 0 and Ain 1 tied to ground, |
| | Ain 2 – Ain 3 as differential inputs |
| | 11: Ain 0 – Ain 1 and Ain 2 – Ain 3 |
| Bit 6: | analogue output active |
| Bit 7: | always 0 |

In order to output an analogue value the address must be sent first and then the control byte. Only then can data be sent to the D/A converter. Once the chip has been addressed it can receive data in an endless loop. Every time the D/A converter is addressed again, the control word must also be re-sent. Accordingly, three bytes are needed for one analogue output.

Listing 12.5 shows the fundamental control for the analogue input Ain 0 and the analogue output Aout. The user inputs the output word with a slider control and receives the measurement result in return. The control byte for the PCF8591 is 64, as only bit 6 (analogue output active) is set.

*Figure 12.9*
*PCF8591*
*analogue inputs*
*and outputs*

*Listing 12.5*
*PCF8591*
*direct control*

```
unit PCF8591;

interface

uses
   I2CCOM2, PORTINC, Windows, Messages, SysUtils, Classes,
   Graphics, Controls, Forms, Dialogs, ExtCtrls, StdCtrls;

type
  TForm1 = class(TForm)
    ScrollBar1: TScrollBar;  Edit1: TEdit;
    Label1: TLabel; Label2: TLabel;
    Edit2: TEdit; Timer1: TTimer;
    procedure FormCreate(Sender: TObject);
    procedure Timer1Timer(Sender: TObject);
    procedure ScrollBar1Change(Sender: TObject);
  end;

var
  Form1: TForm1;

implementation

{$R *.DFM}

procedure DAout (Controlbyte, Value: Byte); begin
  Start;
  Output (72 * 2);          { Address 72, write }
  Output (Controlbyte);
  Output (Value);
  Stop;
end;
```

**continued on following page ...**

**179**

```
function ADin: Byte;
begin
  Start;
  Output (72 * 2 + 1);   { Address 72, read }
  ADin := Inread;
  NoAcknowledge;
  Stop;
end;

procedure TForm1.FormCreate(Sender: TObject);
begin
  I2C_Init;
end;

procedure TForm1.Timer1Timer(Sender: TObject);
begin
  DAout (64,ScrollBar1.Position);
  Edit2.Text := FloatToStr (ADin);
end;

procedure TForm1.ScrollBar1Change(Sender: TObject);
begin
  Edit1.Text := FloatToStr (ScrollBar1.Position);
end;

end.
```

## 12.6  Storage oscilloscope

The analogue converter PCF8591 can be controlled automatically in order to achieve faster measurement sampling. When only measuring, and with no data output, repeated addressing of the chip should be avoided. In this manner sampling rates up to 10 kHz can be achieved.

Listing 12.6 shows a program for fast measurement on all four channels. Simultaneously a function generator is realised. From a prepared value table analogues value are output. With the possibility of analogue in and output the PC8591 is well suited for examination of analogue circuits and Figure 12.10 shows the principle. Via the analogue output a signal waveform is generated

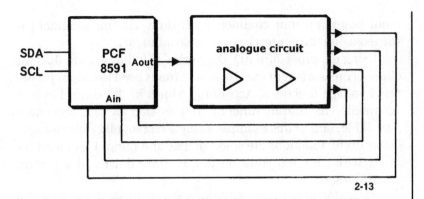

SDA — PCF 8591 Aout

SCL —

Ain

analogue circuit

2-13

*Figure 12.10*

*Using a function
generator and
storage
oscilloscope
to investigate
analogue circuits*

which is passed to the measurement object. The response of the measurement object can be observed on four measurement channels. In this manner, for example, an amplifier's linearity or a filter circuit response can be examined.

Before the A/D Converter can be used the control byte must be sent via the procedure "DAout" in order to select the operation mode and the active channel. Then the readout of measurement results can be performed by the procedure "Adin2". The A/D converter presents its first byte result immediately after the addressing. However, it must be borne in mind the conversion takes place using the same clock signal as for data reading. This is why the result of the previous conversion is always obtained. If an input voltage is to be measured after a longer period of time then it is necessary to read two data bytes and ignore the first.

The procedure 'AD_Series' shows the execution of a faster, four channel measurement series without utilisation of analogue outputs. The control byte (4+1) determines the automatic switching of input channels, where channel 1 is the starting channel and the D/A converter remains switched off. As every conversion is executed during data transfer, after addressing one idle measurement must be executed.

After that as many values can be read as needed without re-sending the address, and conversion rates up to 10 kHz are achieved. The procedure provides a data field with 1000 measurement points on four channels each time. The measurement is started using the control button 'Measurement'.

Using the procedure 'AD_DA_Series' simultaneous to the four channel measurement the D/A-converter is used to output predefined voltage functions. Accordingly, bit 6 in the control byte is activated. The output function is prepared by the procedure 'DA_Table', and in this example a single rectangular pulse is used. Other useful functions are sine, triangle and ramp. This measurement with simultaneous output is started with the button 'Measurement2'.

As analogue outputs and inputs are performed one after the other the converter has to be re-addressed for every conversion. After each output, five measurements follow, where the first result must be neglected as it still represents the response to the previous analogue output.

The program includes graphical measurement output in a window of $500 \times 255$ pixels. Each discrete measurement channel can be written to the screen by pressing buttons K1 to K4; the results of a measurement are shown in Figure 12.11. File output is also possible, with all measurement data saved to a file in tabular form that can be post-processed by other software such as Excel.

*Figure 12.11*
*Measuring a multistage low- pass filter*

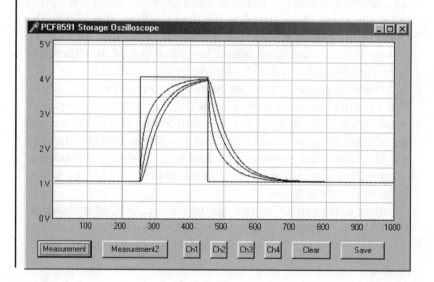

**Listing 12.6** *Storage oscilloscope program with function generator*

```
unit Osci;

interface

uses 2CCOM2,PORTINC,Windows,Messages,SysUtils,Classes,
  Graphics,Controls,Forms,Dialogs, StdCtrls,ExtCtrls;

type
  TForm1 = class(TForm)
    PaintBox1: TPaintBox; Measurement: TButton;
    Measurement2: TButton; K1: TButton;
    K2: TButton; K3: TButton;
    K4: TButton; Store: TButton;
    Clear: TButton;
    procedure FormCreate(Sender: TObject);
    procedure MeasurementClick(Sender: TObject);
    procedure Ch1Click(Sender: TObject);
    procedure Ch2Click(Sender: TObject);
    procedure Ch3Click(Sender: TObject);
    procedure Ch4Click(Sender: TObject);
    procedure Measurement2Click(Sender: TObject);
    procedure SaveClick(Sender: TObject);
    procedure ClearClick(Sender: TObject);
  end;

var
  Form1: TForm1;
  Buffer : Array [1..4000] of Byte;
  DA_Buffer : Array [1..1000] of Byte;

implementation

{$R *.DFM}

procedure DAout (Controlbyte, Value: Byte); begin
  Start;
  Output (72 * 2);                        { Address 72, write }
  Output (Controlbyte);
  Output (Value);
  Stop;
end;
```

*continued on following page ...*

```
function ADin: Byte;
begin
  Start;
  Output (72 * 2 + 1);                        { Address 72, read }
  ADin := Inread;
  NoAcknowledge;
  Stop;
end;

procedure AD_Series;
var n: Integer;
    Dummy : Byte;
begin
  DAout (5,100);                              { Control byte=5 }
  Start;
  Output (72 * 2 + 1);                        { Address 72, read }
  RealTime (True);
  Dummy := Inread;
  Acknowledge;
  for n := 1 to 4000 do begin
    Buffer [n] := Inread;                     { 4000 bytes read in }
    Acknowledge;
  end;
  RealTime (False);
  Dummy := Inread;
  NoAcknowledge;
  Stop;
end;

procedure DA_Table;
var n : Integer;
begin
  for n := 1 to 250 do DA_Buffer [n] := 55;
  for n := 251 to 450 do DA_Buffer [n] := 205;
  for n := 451 to 1000 do DA_Buffer [n] := 55;
end;
```

*continued on following page ...*

```
procedure AD_DA_Series;
var n: Integer;
    Dummy : Byte;
begin
  RealTime(true);
  for n := 1 to 1000 do begin
    DAout (69,DA_Buffer[n]);                    { Control byte = 69 }
    Start;
    Output (72 * 2 + 1);                        { Address 72, read }
    Dummy := Inread; Acknowledge;
    Buffer [4*(n-1)+1] := Inread; Acknowledge;
    DelayUs(10);
    Buffer [4*(n-1)+2] := Inread; Acknowledge;
    DelayUs(10);
    Buffer [4*(n-1)+3] := Inread; Acknowledge;
    DelayUs(10);
    Buffer [4*(n-1)+4] := Inread; NoAcknowledge;
    DelayUs(20);
    Stop;
  end;
  RealTime(False);
end;

procedure StoreTable (Fileiname :String);
var  f : Text;
     n, r : Integer;
begin
  AssignFile(f,Filename);
  {$I-} ReWrite(f); {$I+}
  r := IOresult;
  if  r = 0 then begin
    for n:=0 to 999 do begin;
       write (f,Buffer [4*n+1],#9);
       write (f,Buffer [4*n+2],#9);
       write (f,Buffer [4*n+3],#9);
       writeln (f,Buffer [4*n+4]);
    end;
    CloseFile (f);
  end;
end;
```

*continued on following page ...*

```
procedure TForm1.FormCreate(Sender: TObject);
begin
  I2C_Init;
  DA_Table;
end;

procedure DiagramInit;
var n: Integer;
begin
  with Form1.Paintbox1.Canvas do begin
  Pen.Color:=ClBlack;
  Brush.Color:=ClWhite;
  Rectangle(30,0,531,257);
  Pen.Color:=ClLtGray;
  for n:= 1 to 10 do begin
      MoveTo(31,256-n*25);
      Lineto (529,256-n*25);
  end;
  Brush.Color:=ClLtGray;
  for n:= 0 to 5 do begin
    TextOut(10,250-n*50,FloatToStr(n)+' V');
  end;
  for n:= 1 to 9 do begin
      MoveTo(30+50*n,254);
      Lineto (30+50*n,0)
  end;
  for n:= 1 to 10 do begin
    TextOut(20+50*n,260,FloatToStr(n*100));
  end;
  end;
end;

procedure Plot (Channel: Integer);
var i: Integer;
begin
  with Form1.Paintbox1.Canvas do begin
    Pen.Color:=ClBlack;
    MoveTo (31,256-Buffer[4+Channel]);
    for i := 1 to 999 do
      LineTo (31+i div 2,256-Buffer[i*4+Channel]);
  end;
end;
```

*continued on following page ...*

```
procedure TForm1.MeasurementClick(Sender: TObject);
begin
  DiagramInit;
  AD_Series;
end;
procedure TForm1.Ch1Click(Sender: TObject);
begin
  plot(0);
end;

procedure TForm1.Ch2Click(Sender: TObject);
begin
  Plot (1);
end;

procedure TForm1.Ch3Click(Sender: TObject);
begin
  Plot(2);
end;

procedure TForm1.Ch4Click(Sender: TObject);
begin
  Plot(3);
end;

procedure TForm1.Measurement2Click(Sender: TObject);
begin
  DiagrammInit;
  AD_DA_Series;
end;

procedure TForm1.SaveClick(Sender: TObject);
begin
  StoreTable('Output.dat');
end;

procedure TForm1.ClearClick(Sender: TObject);
begin
  DiagramInit;
end;

end.
```

# 13

# The Joystick Port

Many PC's are endowed with a 15-pin joystick connector, which is also referred to as the game port. This interface often remains unused, whilst all serial and parallel interfaces are connected with peripheral equipment. Accordingly, it is instructive to examine the possibilities of using the joystick port for measurement and control.

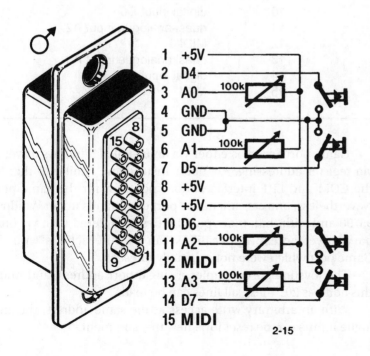

*Figure 13.1*
*Joystick port connector pin assignments*

1 +5V
2 D4
3 A0
4 GND
5 GND
6 A1
7 D5
8 +5V
9 +5V
10 D6
11 A2
12 MIDI
13 A3
14 D7
15 MIDI

2-15

## 13.1 Analogue and digital inputs

The joystick port has four quasi-analogue inputs (A0...A3), making resistance measurement possible by its relationship with the charging time of four capacitors. In addition, four digital inputs (D4–D7) are available. The joystick connector conveys the standard 5-V PC supply voltage to the outside world, providing power to external circuits. Connector allocations are shown in Figure 13.1 and the following table.

| Pin | Connection |
|-----|------------|
| 1,8,9 | Operating voltage +5V |
| 4,5 | GND |
| 2 | digital input D4 |
| 3 | quasi-analogue input A0 |
| 6 | quasi-analogue input A1 |
| 7 | digital input D5 |
| 10 | digital input D6 |
| 11 | quasi-analogue input A2 |
| 12 | MIDI |
| 13 | quasi analogue input A3 |
| 14 | digital input D7 |
| 15 | MIDI |

Game port access is either via an installed Windows driver or via register addressing. An 'open' instruction, similar to that for the COM and LPT interfaces, does not exist for the game port. Nevertheless, one can still utilise port commands under Windows 95/98 and with that, more possibilities are offered than via ordinary driver access. Applications can execute actions with the Game port which were not originally foreseen.

The joystick port occupies a single port address, and under this address 201 (hex), all lines can be read.

With an arbitrary write access at the same address, the analogue inputs can be reset for a new measurement.

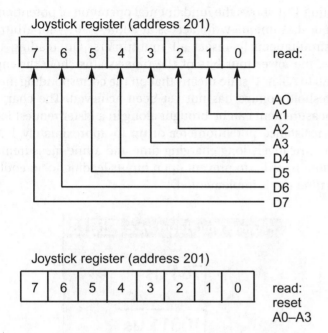

The quasi-analogue inputs are normally used for measuring the resistance of a potentiometer (0 to 100 kΩ). After software initialisation, each resistor charges a 10 nF capacitor. As soon as a charge level of 2/3 of the supply voltage is achieved, an internal comparator trips and the capacitor is discharged. The capacitor charging time is related to the resistance measurement (see Chapter 5.1). Internally, quad 558 timers are mostly used, and inputs are protected by 2.2-kΩ series resistors.

A few newer game ports are integrated onto sound cards and use a modified circuit with an input comparator and charging transistor, instead of timer chips. On measurement initialisation a short pulse is sent to discharge the input capacitor. The input reads the status in the same way as the original timer circuit. Attainment of a switching limit does not however automatically lead to capacitor discharging. This leads to a capacitor voltage in a quiescent state of about 5 V, in contrast to 0 V for the 558 timer circuit. Only a new read process discharges the capacitor instantaneously and starts a new charging process.

Listing 13.1 shows the fundamental operation of potentiometers request. A unique write access at address 201 with arbitrary data, simultaneously resets all four timers. On reading this address, the lower four bits of the timer status show the input states A0 to A3. A '1' state means that on the corresponding input, the threshold voltage has not yet been achieved. The charging time measurement can be brought along in a faster request loop. A high-resistance potentiometer of up to approximately 1 MΩ leads to a relatively long charging time and a fine measurement resolution. In order to prevent open inputs leading to an endless loop, a time-out is implemented.

*Figure 13.2*

*Measurement value on four input channels*

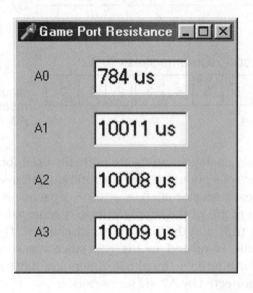

*Listing 13.1*

*Charging time measurement with four external resistances*

```
unit Joy1;

interface

uses
   PORTINC, Windows, Messages, SysUtils, Classes, Graphics,
   Controls, Forms, Dialogs, StdCtrls, ComCtrls, ExtCtrls;
```

***continued on following page ...***

```
type
  TForm1 = class(TForm)
    Timer1: TTimer;      Edit1: TEdit;
    Edit2: TEdit;        Edit3: TEdit;
    Edit4: TEdit;        Label1: TLabel;
    Label2: TLabel;      Label3: TLabel;
    Label4: TLabel;
    procedure Timer1Timer(Sender: TObject);
  end;

var
  Form1: TForm1;

implementation

{$R *.DFM}

function Counter (Channel : Integer) : Word;
var Portvalue : Byte;
begin
  Portvalue := 1;                            { A0 }
  if Channel=2 then Portvalue := 2;          { A1 }
  if Channel=3 then Portvalue := 4;          { A2 }
  if Channel=4 then Portvalue := 8;          { A3 }
  RealTime (true);
  TimeInitus;
  OutPort($201,0);                           { Timer reset }
  While((InPort ($201) and Portvalue) = PortValue)
    and (TimeReadus < 10000) do;
  Counter:=TimeReadus;
  RealTime (false);
end;

procedure TForm1.Timer1Timer(Sender: TObject);
var Output:String;
    Time: DWord;
begin
  Edit1.Text := FloatToStr(Counter(1)) + ' us';
  Edit2.Text := FloatToStr(Counter(2)) + ' us';
  Edit3.Text := FloatToStr(Counter(3)) + ' us';
  Edit4.Text := FloatToStr(Counter(4)) + ' us';
end;

    end.
```

The analogue inputs are suitable for direct resistance measurements, although the basic accuracy is low. This is due to charging capacitor tolerances, and one must therefore calibrate each individual input. For example, direct temperature measurement with NTC resistors of around 100 kΩ is possible.

All four digital inputs are TTL with 1-kΩ pull-up resistors and 47-pF interference suppression capacitors. In the open state, ones are read. The inputs are designed to read external switches connected to ground, but they can also be driven by TTL outputs or transistors. Listing 13.2 shows a simple program for polling the digital inputs, which at the same time shows the states of the analogue inputs.

*Figure 13.3*
*Reading the joystick port*

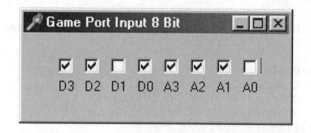

*Listing 13.2*
*Reading of four digital input switches*

```
Unit Joy2;

interface

uses PORTINC,  Windows, Messages, SysUtils, Classes,
   Graphics, Controls, Forms, Dialogs, ExtCtrls, StdCtrls;

type
   TForm1 = class(TForm)
      CheckBox1: TCheckBox;    CheckBox2: TCheckBox;
      CheckBox3: TCheckBox;    CheckBox4: TCheckBox;
      CheckBox5: TCheckBox;    CheckBox6: TCheckBox;
      CheckBox7: TCheckBox;    CheckBox8: TCheckBox;
```

**continued on following page ...**

```
      Label1:  TLabel;   Label2:  TLabel;
      Label3:  TLabel;   Label4:  TLabel;
      Label5:  TLabel;   Label6:  TLabel;
      Label7:  TLabel;   Label8:  TLabel;
      Timer1:  TTimer;
      procedure Timer1Timer(Sender:  TObject);
   end;

var
   Form1:  TForm1;

implementation

{$R *.DFM}

procedure TForm1.Timer1Timer(Sender:  TObject);
var Value: Byte;
begin
   Value := InPort ($201);
   CheckBox1.Checked := ((Value And 1)  >0);
   CheckBox2.Checked := ((Value And 2)  >0);
   CheckBox3.Checked := ((Value And 4)  >0);
   CheckBox4.Checked := ((Value And 8)  >0);
   CheckBox5.Checked := ((Value And 16)  >0);
   CheckBox6.Checked := ((Value And 32)  >0);
   CheckBox7.Checked := ((Value And 64)  >0);
   CheckBox8.Checked := ((Value And 128)  >0);
end;

end.
```

Due to the pull-up resistors used, a relatively large current of approximately 5 mA is drawn by low inputs. This is an advantage for switch poling, but it can lead to problems with CMOS output ports. A few applications therefore require an input driver.

Experiments with digital inputs, as introduced above using the serial interface, can also be undertaken with the game port. However, as with the printer interface, there is a risk of damage to this interface, primarily as the result of overloads. Particular care must be taken to in dealing with the supply voltage pin, since a short circuit can damage the PC!

## 13.2 Voltage measurement

Game port analogue inputs, permit a very simple voltage measurement. Instead of a resistance variation, a voltage change also leads to a change of charging time. However, the charging voltage must fundamentally be over 3.3V. Figure 13.4 shows the connection of measurement inputs to terminal A3. So that null Volt potential is also measurable, measured voltage must be applied relative to the computer operating voltages. The charging resistance is divided, and with that the measurement cable touch of computer-earth does not originate a short circuit. Unfortunately with this simple circuit only measurement of potential free measurement objects is possible, e.g., batteries.

*Figure 13.4*

*Joystick port voltage input*

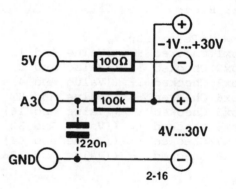

If the measurement voltage is always greater than 4 V in a particular application, it can also be measured with reference to ground. The program in Listing 13.3 shows both possibilities. The variable 'Nullvalue' comprises the envisaged preset counter value of a neutral measurement and an input voltage 5 V respectively with shorted input, when measured relative to the operating voltage. This counter value must be fixed for each individual computer, for example by the sample program in Listing 13.1. The null value of 740 μs was experimentally fixed for input 4. The button 'Zero' permits additional adjustment during ongoing operations. When more input voltages are used the individual values of Nullvalue must be set for each channel.

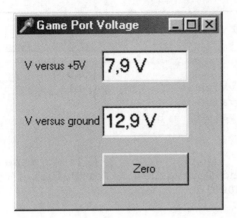

*Figure 13.5*
*Measuring*
*voltages*
*with the*
*game port*

*Listing 13.3*
*Measuring*
*voltages*
*via the*
*joystick port*

```
unit Joy3;

interface

uses
   PORTINC, Windows, Messages, SysUtils, Classes, Graphics,
   Controls, Forms, Dialogs,  StdCtrls, ComCtrls, ExtCtrls;

type
   TForm1 = class(TForm)
     Timer1: TTimer; Edit1: TEdit;
     Edit2: TEdit; Label1: TLabel;
     Label2: TLabel; Button1: TButton;
     procedure FormCreate(Sender: TObject);
     procedure Timer1Timer(Sender: TObject);
     procedure Button1Click(Sender: TObject);
   end;

var
   Form1: TForm1;
   Nullvalue: Integer;

implementation

{$R *.DFM}
```

***continued on following page . . .***

# 13 The Joystick Port

```
function Counter (Channel : Integer) : Word;
var Portvalue : Byte;
begin
  Portvalue := 1;                            { A0 }
  if Channel=2 then Portvalue := 2;          { A1 }
  if Channel=3 then Portvalue := 4;          { A2 }
  if Channel=4 then Portvalue := 8;          { A3 }
  RealTime (true);
  TimeInitus;
  OutPort($201,0);                           { Timer reset }
  While((InPort ($201) and Portvalue) = PortValue)
    and (TimeReadus < 10000)do;
  Counter:=TimeReadus;
  RealTime (false);
end;

procedure TForm1.FormCreate(Sender: TObject);
begin
  Nullvalue := 740;
end;

procedure TForm1.Timer1Timer(Sender: TObject);
var U: Real;
    Output:String;
begin
  U := 3.33 * (1/(1-exp(-Counter(4)/Nullvalue))-1/(1-exp(-1)));
  Edit1.Text := FloatToStrF(U,ffNumber,3,1) + ' V';
  Edit2.Text := FloatToStrF((U+5),ffNumber,3,1) + ' V';
end;

procedure TForm1.Button1Click(Sender: TObject);
begin
  Nullvalue := Counter(4);
end;

end.
```

The relationship between counter value and voltage is non linear, but it can be modelled with an exponential function. The virtual formula and linearisation is executed in the Timer procedure, and it resembles the linearisation of simple A/D converters described in Chapter 5.2.

The introduced measurement method has only a very limited accuracy. The primary error sources are the computer supply voltage and the temperature coefficients of the internal capacitors. With an effective resolution of 0.1 V and a measurement range of approximately 30 V, it is however sufficient for many applications.

Resolution and accuracy can be further improved by external 0.22-µF capacitors (Figure 13.4), when a traditional game port with 558 timers is used. Through these measures, longer charging times and correspondingly greater counter values are achieved, so that voltage can be resolved into smaller steps. Apart from that, long term stability can be improved by the use of foil capacitors with more suitable temperature coefficients. One has no influence however, on the inaccuracy caused by the PC's operating voltage. With the modified circuit, which occurs on some Sound cards, no external capacitor can be used because the brief charging pulse is insufficient, to discharge the external capacitor completely.

## 13.3  Threshold monitoring

A useful property of the game port with 558 timer is that the analogue input status (trigger threshold achieved / not achieved) is stored fully independent from other applications in flip flops. One can therefore at any time, reset the timer and permit another PC process to use the PC processor. At any time one can query if the limit of 3.3 V was reached at least once.

Figure 13.6 (overleaf) shows possible applications of limit supervision, greater voltages being possible when using a voltage divider. An NTC resistor can be used to monitor a temperature limit. A possible application is temperature monitoring in the PC itself. The measurement sensor can be fastened to a discrete IC, to determine whether sufficient cooling exists.

Apart from the monitoring of analogue quantities, it can also monitor a discrete pulse of at least circa 2 ms or a switch status. In each case one can examine later, if fixed results occurred at least once. Listing 13.4 shows a possible program for limit supervision, where one can reset and report inputs arbitrarily at any time.

*Figure 13.6*
*Threshold*
*monitoring with*
*the game port*

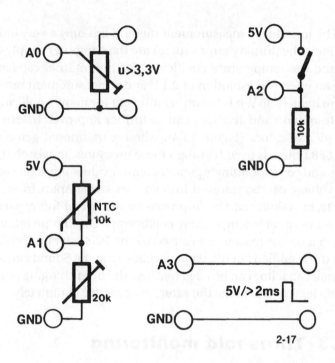

With the classical game port and its 558 timer, the input voltage may return to zero after reaching the 3.3-V threshold, as the status remains stored in the flip-flop. The modified input circuit used in some sound cards, however, employs a Schmitt trigger input with thresholds of 1.7 V and 3.3 V. After reaching the upper limit, the voltage may not drop below 1.7 V if the status is to be held. Especially when polling switches or sampling individual pulses, this has to be ensured by the use of a suitable voltage divider, since otherwise only momentary states can be shown.

*Figure 13.7*
*Threshold value*
*polling*

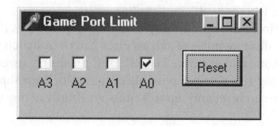

*Listing 13.4* *A program for monitoring threshold values*

```
unit Joy4;

interface

uses
  PORTINC, Windows, Messages, SysUtils, Classes, Graphics,
  Controls, Forms, Dialogs, ExtCtrls, StdCtrls;

type
  TForm1 = class(TForm)
    CheckBox1: TCheckBox;    CheckBox2: TCheckBox;
    CheckBox3: TCheckBox;    CheckBox4: TCheckBox;
    Label1: TLabel;    Label2: TLabel;
    Label3: TLabel;    Label4: TLabel;
    Timer1: TTimer;    Button1: TButton;
    procedure Timer1Timer(Sender: TObject);
    procedure FormCreate(Sender: TObject);
    procedure Button1Click(Sender: TObject);
  end;

var
  Form1: TForm1;

implementation

{$R *.DFM}

procedure TForm1.Timer1Timer(Sender: TObject);
var Value: Byte;
begin
  Value := InPort ($201);
  CheckBox1.Checked := ((Value And 1) =0);
  CheckBox2.Checked := ((Value And 2) =0);
  CheckBox3.Checked := ((Value And 4) =0);
  CheckBox4.Checked := ((Value And 8) =0);
end;
```

*continued on following page . . .*

```
procedure TForm1.FormCreate(Sender: TObject);
begin
  OutPort ($201,0);
end;

procedure TForm1.Button1Click(Sender: TObject);
begin
  OutPort ($201,0);
end;

end.
```

## 13.4  Switched output

The possibilities for game port usage are unfortunately very limited due to lack of any digital output. However, using a small additional circuit one output can be built. Fortunately on analogue inputs of the classical game port, single saw tooth pulses can be generated if a resistor is connected to the operating voltage. Many such pulses have an average potential of 2 V, sufficient to switch a transistor.

Figure 13.8 shows a transistor circuit used to create an output. The transistor switches an LED on, when concurrent reset commands are passed to the Joystick timer. An additional capacitor filters out remaining ripples, caused by the switching pulses. By using a 2.2-µF capacitor, 'soft' switching of the LED is achieved.

Listing 13.5 shows the program for an LED blinker. In the timer procedure a series of reset pulses with a spacing of only 10 µs is generated. Through this 'non-stop firing' the transistor is switched on. As soon as the reset commands are omitted, the transistor is switched off, and it starts blinking with a period of one second. By starting and stopping the timers, the blinking can be switched on and off.

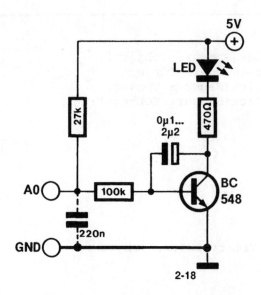

*Figure 13.8*
*Switch output*
*connected to*
*the game port*

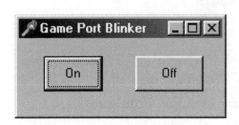

*Figure 13.9*
*Output via the*
*game port*

*Listing 13.5*
*Output driver*
*program*

```
unit Joy5;

interface

uses PORTINC, Windows, Messages, SysUtils, Classes,
   Graphics, Controls, Forms, Dialogs, ExtCtrls, StdCtrls;

type
  TForm1 = class(TForm)
    Timer1: TTimer;
    Button1: TButton;
```

**continued on following page ...**

**203**

```
    Button2: TButton;
    procedure Timer1Timer(Sender: TObject);
    procedure FormCreate(Sender: TObject);
    procedure Button1Click(Sender: TObject);
    procedure Button2Click(Sender: TObject);
  end;

var
  Form1: TForm1;

implementation

{$R *.DFM}

procedure TForm1.Timer1Timer(Sender: TObject);
var n: Integer;
begin
  RealTime(true);
  for n:= 1 to 10000 do begin
    OutPort($201,0);
    DelayUs (10);
  end;
  RealTime(false);
end;

procedure TForm1.FormCreate(Sender: TObject);
begin
  Timer1.Interval:= 1000;
  Timer1.Enabled := true;
end;

procedure TForm1.Button1Click(Sender: TObject);
begin
  Timer1.Enabled := true;
end;

procedure TForm1.Button2Click(Sender: TObject);
begin
  Timer1.Enabled := false;
end;

end.
```

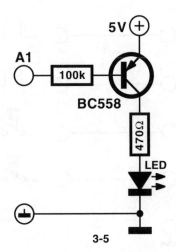

*Figure 13.10*
*Modified*
*driver stage*
*for modern*
*game ports*

The previously mentioned modified game port adapter with a 5-V quiescent state requires a different driver circuit. The use of a PNP transistor leads overall to a simple construction. The transistor is switched on, as long as write pulses faster than approximately once per millisecond continue.

## 13.5  Digital counter

Through direct interrogation of digital input, the Joystick ports can realise many forms of digital counters. The digital input as per Figure 13.11, can be directly connected to a switch or TTL-output. Those in Chapter 6, described frequency measurement can be applied with adaptation of the port address also for these ports. Here, for a change an event counter shall be introduced, that of course can be programmed for the serial interface in the same manner.

Listing 13.6 shows the program for a quad pulse counter. All four inputs were simultaneously observed in the timer procedure, where incoming pulses are counted and displayed independently. The counter is designed for slow events. An interval time of 20ms produces the maximum pulse frequency of 25 Hz.

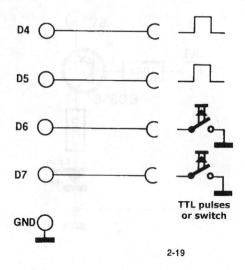

**Figure 13.11**
*Reading in
pulses or
switch states*

TTL pulses
or switch

2-19

These inputs are appropriate for the direct connection of switches, keys or reed contacts. The frequently observed phenomenon of 'contact bounce' can lead to counting errors. An effective countermeasure is to delay the input polling according to the clock rate of Timer1, whose period can be increased if necessary. If the pulses originate from an electronic source, such as a Geiger-Müller counter tube or an oscillator, the shortest possible delay should be used in order to achieve a high upper frequency limit and allow short pulses to be properly recognised.

**Figure 13.12**
*Four
independent
counters*

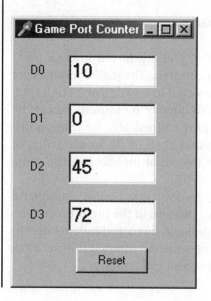

*Listing 13.6  A pulse counter with four input channels on the joystick port*

```
unit Joy6;

interface

uses
   PORTINC, Windows, Messages, SysUtils, Classes, Graphics,
   Controls, Forms, Dialogs, StdCtrls, ComCtrls, ExtCtrls;

type
   TForm1 = class(TForm)
      Timer1: TTimer;   Edit1: TEdit;
      Edit2: TEdit;   Edit3: TEdit;
      Edit4: TEdit;   Label1: TLabel;
      Label2: TLabel;   Label3: TLabel;
      Label4: TLabel;   Button1: TButton;
      procedure FormCreate(Sender: TObject);
      procedure Timer1Timer(Sender: TObject);
      procedure Button1Click(Sender: TObject);
   end;

var
   Form1: TForm1;
   z1,z2,z3,z4: word;
   Input, InputOld: Byte;

implementation

{$R *.DFM}

procedure TForm1.FormCreate(Sender: TObject);
begin
   Z1:=0; Z2:=0; Z3:=0; Z4:=0;
   InputOld := InPort($201);
   Timer1.Interval := 20;
   Timer1.Enabled := True;
end;
procedure TForm1.Timer1Timer(Sender: TObject);
begin
   Input := InPort($201);
```

*continued on following page . . .*

```
    if (Input and 16) < (InputOld and 16) then
       Z1 := Z1 + 1;
    if (Input and 32) < (InputOld and 32) then
       Z2 := Z2 + 1;
    if (Input and 64) < (InputOld and 64) then
       Z3 := Z3 + 1;
    if (Input and 128) < (InputOld and 128) then
       Z4 := Z4 + 1;
    InputOld := Input;
    Edit1.Text := FloatToStr(Z1);
    Edit2.Text := FloatToStr(Z2);
    Edit3.Text := FloatToStr(Z3);
    Edit4.Text := FloatToStr(Z4);
end;

procedure TForm1.Button1Click(Sender: TObject);
begin
   Z1:=0; Z2:=0; Z3:=0; Z4:=0;
   InputOld := InPort($201);
end;

end.
```

## 13.6 Joystick driver calls

Up to now, all programs have accessed the game adapter hardware via direct port commands. There is still also, the official method, with the Windows driver. PORT.DLL contains the important routines, ready for use in Visual Basic:

| | |
|---|---|
| JoyX | provides the position on A1 |
| JoyY | provides the position on A2 |
| JoyZ | provides the position on A3 |
| JoyU | provides the position on A4 |
| JoyButton | provides the actual pressed key on D1–D4 |

For these functions to be utilised, the joystick must first be correctly installed. Windows only recognises a joystick if all pots are connected. You can avoid purchasing a genuine joystick by connecting fixed 47-kΩ resistors between the analogue inputs and +5 V just for the installation process. The following assumes that a two-axis joystick has been installed, so only JoyX and JoyY polling are functional. Also, when the program is running, JoyX and JoyY polling are active only if resistors are present on both inputs. If a program is supposed to use only one analogue input, a second resistor of around 100 kΩ must still be connected, otherwise the result will always be zero.

Even though a joystick is installed under Windows, direct access via port commands, will still work as before. There is no access check as with the serial interface or the printer port, at least under Windows 95 and Windows 98. Two programs can even be started simultaneously, one using port commands and the other with driver access to the game port. Obviously Microsoft does not consider the game port to be a security-critical interface.

The following small Visual Basic program demonstrates driver calls for the X and Y pots and the joystick buttons. Port polling always returns only one button (1–4). If for example D1 and D3 are simultaneously switched to ground, only '1' is returned. Simultaneous testing of several digital inputs with port polling is not possible here.

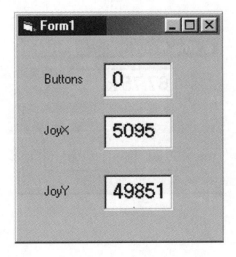

*Figure 13.13*
*Joystick polling*
*via a driver*

```
Private Sub Timer1_Timer()
   Text1.Text = Str$(JOYBUTTON())
   Text2.Text = Str$(JOYX())
   Text3.Text = Str$(JOYY())
End Sub
```

*Listing 13.7*

*Output of polled values from the game port*

A simple ohmmeter can be constructed using Visual Basic. The value of the resistor under test is calculated from the value read in via Joy Y. There is a linear relationship between these two quantities, with the zero point being determined by the value of the internal protection resistor on the analogue input. The generally low level of accuracy of the inputs, which is primarily due to the tolerances of the internal charging capacitors, makes individual calibration necessary for each PC.

The program 'Ohmmeter' makes use of two experimentally determined reference values for the null resistance and a measured value of 100 kΩ. However, both reference values can be individually calibrated while the program is running by connecting a suitable reference resistor and clicking on the corresponding calibration button.

*Figure 13.14*

*A simple ohmmeter*

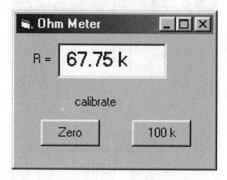

**210**

***Listing 13.8*** *The ohmmeter program*

```
Dim N0
Dim N100

Private Sub Command1_Click()
  N0 = JOYY()
End Sub

Private Sub Command2_Click()
  N100 = JOYY()
End Sub

Private Sub Form_Load()
  N0 = 899
  N100 = 50000
End Sub

Private Sub Timer1_Timer()
  r = (JOYY() - N0) / (N100 - N0) * 100
  r = Int(r * 100) / 100
  Text1.Text = Str$(r) + " k"
End Sub
```

# 14

# The Sound Card

A sound card is now a standard component of practically every PC. It can be used not only for music and speech output, but also for measurement purposes. After all, with a sound card you are in possession of high-quality A/D and D/A converters with 8-bit and 16-bit resolution, ready for use. The card has various inputs and outputs, viz:

- microphone input, usually mono,
- line input, often stereo,
- line output, often stereo,
- speaker output, often stereo.

Sound cards are delivered with a 'mixer' program, which represent a sort of software mixing panel for recording and playback. Under Windows 95, such a mixer is a standard feature; it is represented by a loudspeaker icon in the task bar (SYSTRAY.EXE) when the sound card is correctly installed.

The DLL supports only 8-bit and 16-bit PCM formats, and only monaural recording is possible. As the purpose of the DLL is to gather measurement data, there are not any DLL commands for generating WAVE files. There are already countless other programs that provide this capability.

*Figure 14.1*
*The Win95*
*mixer for the*
*Sound Blaster 16*
*sound card*

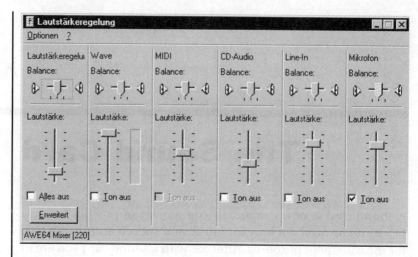

PORT.DLL supports the sound card with the following commands:

| | |
|---|---|
| SOUNDIS | Request whether a sound card is present |
| SOUNDCAPIN | Display the sound formats supported for recording |
| SOUNDCAPOUT | Display the sound formats supported for playback |
| SOUNDIN | Record |
| SOUNDOUT | Playback |
| SOUNDBUSY | Recording in progress |
| SOUNDGETRATE | Request sample-rate |
| SOUNDSETRATE | Set sample rate |
| SOUNDGETBYTES | Request bytes per sample |
| SOUNDSETBYTES | Set bytes per sample |

First of all, with SOUNDIS it can be determined if a general sound card is available, installed in accordance with Windows rules. The function SOUNDIS is already declared in the file PORT-INC.PAS. A brief program demonstrates the call (Listing 14.1).

**Listing 14.1** *Sound card query in Delphi*

```
unit Unit1; //Delphi3

interface

uses PORTINC, Windows, Messages, SysUtils, Classes,
Graphics, Controls, Forms, Dialogs, StdCtrls;

type
  TForm1 = class(TForm)
    Button1: TButton;
    procedure Button1Click(Sender: TObject);

var Form1: TForm1;

implementation

{$R *.DFM}

procedure TForm1.Button1Click(Sender: TObject);
begin
  if SOUNDIS then MessageDlg ('Sound card available.',
     mtInformation,[mbOk], 0)
  else MessageDlg('Sound card not available.',
     mtInformation,[mbOk], 0)
end;

end.
```

After button1 is pressed, sound card availability is displayed in a message box as shown in Figure 14.2.

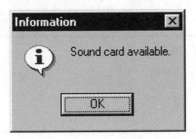

*Figure 14.2*
*Query result*

The sound card can also be addressed in Visual Basic just as easily as in Delphi. In addition to Visual Basic 5, Visual Basic for Applications (VBA) (which supports macro programming in Word or Excel) can also be used (see Chapter 1.2). A query under Word97 runs just as under VB5:

*Listing 14.2*
*Sound card*
*search in Word*

```
Declare Function SOUNDIS Lib "PORT.DLL" () As Integer

Sub test()
    If SOUNDIS = 0 Then MsgBox "Sound card not available"
    Else MsgBox "Sound card available"
End Sub
```

*Figure 14.3*
*Successful access*
*using a Word*
*macro*

Different sound cards support different file formats. Routine SOUNDCAPIN displays a message that indicates the available recording and playback formats. Only the most common WAVE formats are displayed, although other sample rates may be supported. In PORT.DLL, a sample rate of 11.025 kHz and 8-bit mono is set as default.

*Listing 14.3*
*Querying the*
*supported*
*recording*
*formats*

```
Declare Sub CAPIN Lib "PORT.DLL" ()

Sub test()
    CAPIN
End Sub
```

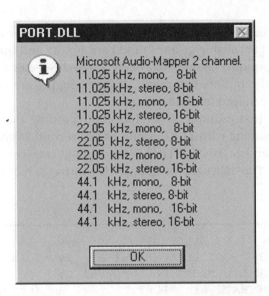

*Figure 14.4*
*Display of recording formats*

## 14.1 Recording and playback

With 8-bit mono recording, a byte is allocated for each sample. For a recording lasting one second, a buffer storage of 11,025 bytes is needed. The DLL must get this buffer storage from the calling program. Additionally the length of buffer is a parameter. In VBA or VB5 the call consists of few lines of code:

*Listing 14.4*
*Recording and playback in VBA (Word97)*

```
Declare Sub SOUNDIN Lib "PORT.DLL" (ByVal A$, ByVal L%)
Declare Sub SOUNDOUT Lib "PORT.DLL" (ByVal A$, ByVal L%)

Sub test()
    A$ = Space$(11025)
    MsgBox "Start Recording.":
    SOUNDIN  A$, 11025
    MsgBox "Start Playback.":
    SOUNDOUT A$, 11025
End Sub
```

The prerequisite for successful recording is, that an audio carrier signal is available at the sound card inputs and the mixer of the corresponding channel has been selected. Specific care is bidden with the buffers committal. If false lengths are committed here, they can lead to difficult crashes.

In the first example as well as the recording then also the playback is done with 11,025 samples per second. With SOUNDSETRATE and SOUNDGETRATE the sample rate can be set or requested. The data can, for example be output at half speed.

*Listing 14.5*
*Playback at half speed*

```
Declare Sub SOUNDIN Lib "PORT.DLL" (ByVal A$, ByVal L%)
Declare Sub SOUNDOUT Lib "PORT.DLL" (ByVal A$, ByVal L%)
Declare Sub SOUNDSETRATE Lib "PORT.DLL" (ByVal L%)
Declare Function SOUNDGETRATE Lib "PORT.DLL" () As Integer

Sub test()
    A$ = Space$(11025)
    MsgBox "Start Recording.":  SOUNDIN A$, 11025
    SOUNDSETRATE SOUNDGETRATE / 2
    MsgBox "Start Playback.":  SOUNDOUT A$, 11025
End Sub
```

## 14.2 An oscilloscope in Excel

The recorded data can not only be used for playback, but also for a meaningful display. With 8-bit mono samples, the sampled data bytes lie in range –127 to 127, 0 to 255 respectively. Silence is confirmed by the value 127. Actual values reach up to 255 or down to 0. Silence on the input results in byte values about 128. A short Word macro (Listing 14.6) displays the first 10 sample values of an 8-bit recording in a message box.

A diagrammatic presentation is more effective than textual output, and with very little effort Excel graphing features can be utilised. In Excel 97 the small macro shown in Listing 14.7 displays 1000 samples in a diagram.

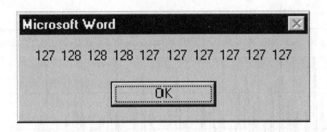

*Figure 14.6*
*Numerical output*

*Listing 14.6*
*Numerical output of sound data*

```
Declare Sub SOUNDIN Lib "PORT.DLL" (ByVal A$, ByVal L%)

Sub test()
    A$ = Space$(10)
    SOUNDIN A$, 10
    For i = 1 To 10
        B$ = B$ + Str(Asc(Mid$(A$, i, 1))) + " "
    Next i
    MsgBox B$
End Sub
```

The macro can be started directly by pressing the button in the sheet. Once the diagram is set up any other call to the macro will update the presentation.

*Listing 14.7*
*Reading measured data from an Excel table*

```
Declare Sub SOUNDIN Lib "PORT.DLL" (ByVal A$, ByVal L%)

Sub test()
    A$ = Space$(1000)
    SOUNDIN A$, 1000
    For i = 1 To 1000
        Cells(i, 1) = Asc(Mid$(A$, i, 1))
    Next i
End Sub
```

**219**

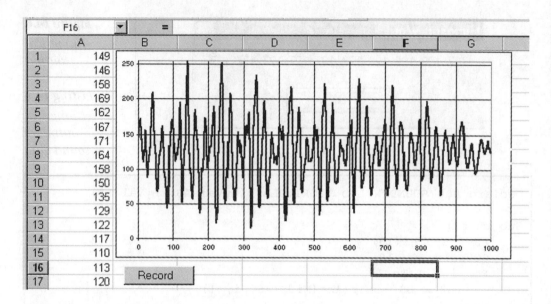

**Figure 14.7**
*Oscillograph
display in Excel*

## 14.3 An oscilloscope in Delphi

It is relatively simple to obtain an adequate representation of
sound data in Excel. To derive a stand alone EXE file, Delphi or
Visual Basic is needed. The following steps show how to draw a
simple graph in a Delphi Paintbox component.

The Paintbox component with a height of 256 pixels is placed
on a new form. This is done by setting the property 'Height' to 256
in the Object Inspector window. The property 'Width' is used later
to fit the sample count into the width of the component. The display is controlled by a Start button (Button1) and a Stop button
(Button2). Both buttons are placed beneath the Paintbox.

The measurement data must be stored in a temporary data
buffer. The program uses two global variables, one for the buffer
and another for its size. On program entry (OnCreate) the buffer is
initialised.

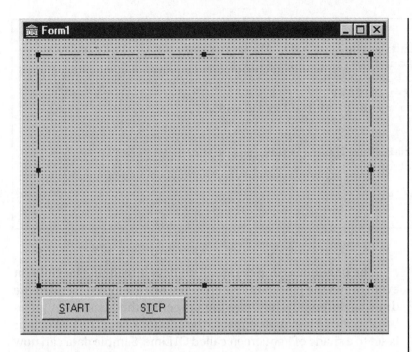

*Figure 14.9*
*Preparing*
*the form*

The first step is to determine if a sound card is present, and the second is to reserve memory with a length equal to the paint-box width. The buffer is initialised by the silence value 127. On exiting the program, memory must be released, and this is done using the OnClose event of Form1.

*Listing 14.8*
*Data buffer*
*usage*

```
implementation

{$R *.DFM}

var
     Buffer:PCHAR;
     Size:Integer;

procedure TForm1.FormCreate(Sender: TObject);
var i:integer;
```

*continued on following page . . .*

```
begin
   if not Soundis then  begin ShowMessage
       ('No Sound Device.');exit;end;
   Size:=paintbox1.width;
   GetMem(Buffer,Size+1);
   for i:=0 to size-1 do buffer[i]:=#127;
end;

procedure TForm1.FormClose(Sender: TObject; var Action:
     TCloseAction);
begin
   FreeMem(Buffer);
end;
```

The paintbox is drawn even if no data is read in. The OnPaint event draws the paintbox content. Previous examples handled the drawing differently, but here the proper method is used. A green brush paints a rectangle equal to the paintbox size. The pen colour is set to a shade of light green called C1Lime. Sample data can now be plotted. On the first run, the start position is set by the MoveTo command, with the entire curve being plotted with LineTo.

*Listing 14.9*

*Measurement data graphical output*

```
procedure TForm1.PaintBox1Paint(Sender: TObject);
var i,x,y,w,h:Integer;
begin
  w:=paintbox1.width;
  h:=paintbox1.height;
  Paintbox1.Canvas.Pen.Color:=ClBlack;
  Paintbox1.Canvas.Brush.Color:=ClGreen;
  PaintBox1.Canvas.Rectangle(0,0,w,h);
  paintbox1.canvas.pen.color:=cllime;
  for i:= 0 to size-1 do
 begin
     x:=i;
     y:=h-ord(Buffer[i]);
     if i=0 then paintbox1.canvas.MoveTo(x,y)
            else paintbox1.canvas.LineTo(x,y);
   end;
end;
```

Pressing the 'Start' button starts sound capture, and the appropriate code is provided for the OnClick event of Button1. When recording is finished, the Paintbox1.Invalidate call declares the Paintbox rectangle to be invalid. This informs Windows that the Paintbox function OnPaint must be called.

*Listing 14.10*
*Data capture and graphing*

```
procedure TForm1.Button1Click(Sender: TObject);
begin
    SOUNDIN(Buffer,size);
    PaintBox1.Invalidate;
end;
```

With the addition of a timer, data can be captured continuously. The Timer1 interval is set to 1 ms to enable fast continuous capture. Timer1 is initially disabled and the OnTimer event of Timer1 performs the capture. The only purpose of the 'Stop' button is to disable Timer1.

*Listing 14.11*
*Control via Timer1*

```
procedure TForm1.Button1Click(Sender: TObject);
begin
    Timer1.Enabled:=      True;
end;
procedure TForm1.Timer1Timer(Sender: TObject);
begin
      SOUNDIN(Buffer,size);
      PaintBox1.Invalidate;
end;
procedure TForm1.Button2Click(Sender: TObject);
begin
      Timer1.Enabled:=False;
end;
```

The program described here represents a very simple oscilloscope. As the green rectangle is drawn on every Timer event there is a slight flicker, which can be avoided by placing the Paintbox on a green panel component, which will cause the flicker to disappear. A more sophisticated method is to draw the entire picture on an invisible bitmap, followed by a bitmap copy to the visible screen, resulting in a steady, flicker-free display.

The CD contains a compiled program which uses this method of captured data display. Some additional analysis is provided with average and rms values being displayed.

*Figure 14.12*

*Oscilloscope with extended features*

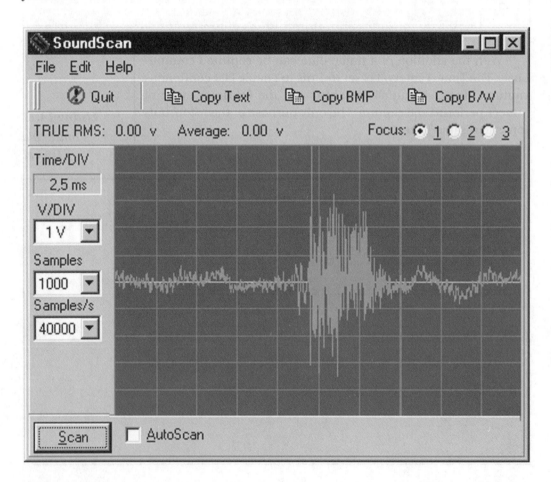

## 14.4  Computed sound output

The sound card can be used not only as a simple oscilloscope, but also to build an oscillator. All output data is transformed into sound by the sound card, so if that data is computed using trigonometrical functions, it is possible to generate a sinusoidal tone. Two tones are generated, one being 8-bit and the other 16-bit, to demonstrate sound quality.

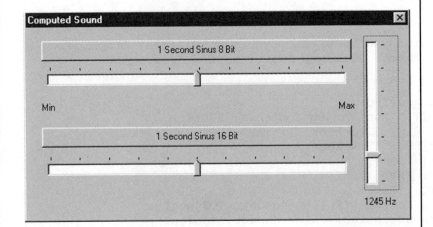

*Figure 14.13*
*Sinusoidal*
*sound output*

Figure 14.13 shows the Delphi program control window for computed tone output. Two horizontal volume sliders set the amplitude, while the vertical slider sets the output frequency.

The programs kernel is the computation of sinusoidal output data using a sampling rate of 22,050 Hz. The 8-bit output is computed in the procedure 'Button8BITClick'. The first step is to allocate 22,050 bytes of memory. TrackBar8Bit.Position with a range of 0 to 127 is the set amplitude. Now the signal data bytes can be computed into the memory buffer using a loop and the appropriate equation. SOUNDSETRATE sets the sample rate, whilst SOUNDSETBYTES(1) informs the DLL that one 8-bit byte sample has been generated.

Output is executed using the SOUNDOUT routine. The global variable Freq is set by sliding the TrackbarFREQ component.

**225**

*Listing 14.14*

*Sinusoidal output in various formats*

The range of the frequency TrackBar is set such that the frequency can be adjusted between 100 Hz and 6000 Hz. The maximum value is 5900 and the minimum value is 0. The 100-Hz offset is taken into account in the computation of the variable 'freq'.

```
unit sine;     //for Delphi3

interface

uses
    PORTINC, Windows, Messages, SysUtils, Classes, Graphics,
    Controls, Forms, Dialogs, StdCtrls, ComCtrls;

type
  TForm1 = class(TForm)
    Button8BIT: TButton; Button16BIT: TButton;
    TrackBar8Bit: TTrackBar; TrackBar16BIT: TTrackBar;
    TrackBarFREQ: TTrackBar;
    LabelMIN: TLabel;
    LabelMAX: TLabel;
    LabelFREQ: TLabel;
    procedure Button8BITClick(Sender: TObject);
    procedure Button16BITClick(Sender: TObject);
    procedure TrackBarFREQChange(Sender: TObject);
  end;

var Form1: TForm1;

implementation

{$R *.DFM}

var freq:Integer=100;
procedure TForm1.Button8BITClick(Sender: TObject);
CONST RATE=22050;
VAR Size,t,amp:Integer; p:pchar;
begin
      GetMem(p,RATE);
      Size:=RATE;
      Amp:= Trackbar8BIT.Position;
```

**continued on following page ...**

```
      For t:= 0 to RATE-1 do
      BEGIN
             p[t]:=chr(Round(127+Amp*sin(2*pi*freq*t/RATE)));
      end;
      SOUNDSetRate(Rate);
      SOUNDSetBytes(1);
      SoundOut(p,Size);
      FreeMem(p);
end;
procedure TForm1.Button16BITClick(Sender: TObject);
CONST RATE=22050;
VAR Size,t,amp,val:Integer; p:pchar;
begin
      GetMem(p,RATE*2);
      Size:=RATE;
      Amp:= Trackbar16BIT.Position;
      For t:= 0 to RATE-1 do
      BEGIN
             val:=Round(0+Amp*sin(2*pi*freq*t/RATE));
             p[t*2]:=chr(LO(val));
             p[t*2+1]:=chr(HI(val));
      end;
      SOUNDSetRate(Rate);
      SOUNDSetBytes(2);
      SoundOut(p,Size);
      FreeMem(p);
end;

procedure TForm1.TrackBarFREQChange(Sender: TObject);
begin
   freq:= 100+trackbarFREQ.max-trackbarFREQ.position;
   labelFREQ.caption:=inttostr(freq)+' Hz';
end;

end.
```

Procedure Button16BITClick calculates 16-bit data for a one-second sinusoidal output. Data is computed in an integer array, as each value consists of two sound bytes. Signal sound quality at a low amplitude is noticeably improved using 16-bit sound output.

## 14.5 Hearing tests using the sound card

The human ear has a wide frequency range and is most sensitive in the 1 kHz to 2 kHz range. Possible hearing loss can be examined by measuring sensitivity to different frequencies.

A simple measurement program can be written for a 16-bit sound card and a headset. This does not provide reliable information about absolute hearing capacity, but it does allow comparative measurements. The youngest family member, not yet exposed to disco music, is most suitable for this exercise. With increasing age a reduction of the upper frequency limit is normal. Ear damage can be seen if there is a serious loss of sensitivity or if significant differences are seen between the two ears. The example below shows some weakness in the vicinity of 5 kHz.

*Figure 14.14*

*Hearing test*

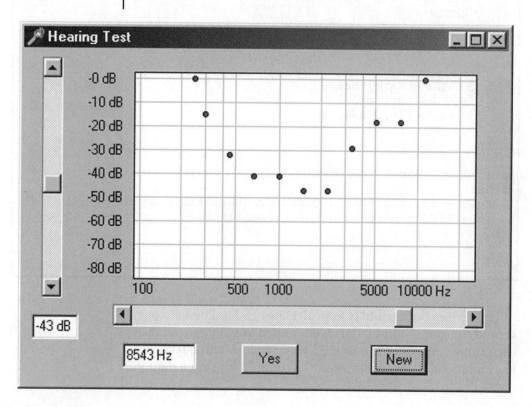

In the program the lowest sound level is used to indicate the sensitivity of that frequency. By pressing the 'Yes' Button this sensitivity is written on the graph. Using the Windows mixer application the master level of sound output can be set to an appropriate level. At highest sensitivity the threshold should still be above –80 dB. The real output volume depends on equipment used i.e. headset and sound card.

A wide dynamic range and the strong loss of sensitivity at low and very high frequencies require a wide level range of 80 dB. Using the master control for volume regulation is not possible, since its transfer characteristic is unknown. The only possibility is to calculate the sound data by frequency and level. The required dynamic range can be obtained using 16-bit output. A output of 32,000 represents the maximum amplitude. The smallest amplitude (3) represents an output voltage that is smaller by a factor of 10,000, and thus a signal that is 80 dB weaker. For sound levels that are not excessively low, a good signal with very low harmonic content can be achieved at 44,100 samples per second, .

The program works with short tone bursts that are repeated two times a second under timer control. The tones cannot be simply switched on and off, since this would generate high-frequency components that would be especially undesirable in the lower frequency range where the higher spectral components would fall in a more sensitive range of the human ear. The sinusoidal signals are therefore faded in and out. The Gaussian error curve $f(x) = \exp(-x^2)$ is used here as the evaluation function.

The program uses a logarithmic scale for both amplitude and frequency, with the slider position matching the diagram scaling.

*Listing 14.15*
*Hearing test*

```
unit Eartest;

interface

uses PortInc,Windows, Messages, SysUtils, Classes,
    Graphics, Controls, Forms, Dialogs, ExtCtrls, StdCtrls;
```

*continued on following page ...*

# 14 The Sound Card

```
type
  TForm1 = class(TForm)
    PaintBox1: TPaintBox;
    ScrollBar1: TScrollBar;
    ScrollBar2: TScrollBar;
    Timer1: TTimer;
    Edit1: TEdit;
    Edit2: TEdit;
    Yes: TButton;
    New: TButton;
    procedure Timer1Timer(Sender: TObject);
    procedure NewClick(Sender: TObject);
    procedure FormCreate(Sender: TObject);
    procedure YesClick(Sender: TObject);
  end;

var
  Form1: TForm1;
  Diagram: Boolean;

implementation

{$R *.DFM}

procedure DiagramInit;
var n: Integer;
begin
  with Form1.Paintbox1.Canvas do begin
  Pen.Color:=ClBlack;
  Brush.Color:=ClWhite;
  Rectangle(40,10,336,185);
  Pen.Color:=ClLtGray;
  for n:= 0 to 8 do begin
       MoveTo(41,15+n*20);
       Lineto (335,15+n*20);
  end;
  Brush.Color:=ClLtGray;
  for n:= 0 to 8 do begin
    TextOut(0,10+n*20,'-'+FloatToStr(n*10)+' dB');
  end;
```

*continued on following page ...*

**230**

```
  for n:= 0 to 2 do begin
      MoveTo(45+120*n,183); Lineto (45+120*n,10);
      MoveTo(45+120*n+36,183); Lineto (45+120*n+36,10);
      MoveTo(45+120*n+57,183); Lineto (45+120*n+57,10);
      MoveTo(45+120*n+72,183); Lineto (45+120*n+72,10);
      MoveTo(45+120*n+83,183); Lineto (45+120*n+83,10);
  end;
  TextOut(40+00,187,'100');
  TextOut(40+83,187,'500');
  TextOut(35+120,187,'1000');
  TextOut(35+203,187,'5000');
  TextOut(30+240,187,'10000 Hz');
  end;
  Diagram := true;
end;

procedure TForm1.Timer1Timer(Sender: TObject);
CONST RATE=44100;
VAR Size,t,val:Integer;
    Amp, Freq, Gauss: Real;
    p:pchar;
begin
    if not Diagram then DiagramInit;
    Size:=RATE div 4;
    GetMem(p,Size*2);
    Amp := 32000 / exp(ScrollBar2.Position/20*ln(10));
    Edit2.Text := '-'+FloatToStr(ScrollBar2.Position)+' dB' ;
    Freq := round (100* exp(ScrollBar1.Position/12*ln(2)));
    Edit1.Text := FloatToStr(Freq)+ ' Hz';
    For t:= 0 to Size -1 do
    BEGIN
        Gauss := exp(-1*(sqr((t-Size/2)/Size*4)));
        val:=Round(0+Amp*Gauss*sin(2*pi*freq*t/RATE));
        p[t*2]:=chr(LO(val));
        p[t*2+1]:=chr(HI(val));
    end;
    SoundSetRate(Rate);
    SoundSetBytes(2);
    SoundOut(p,Size);
    FreeMem(p);
end;
```

*continued on following page ...*

```
procedure TForm1.NewClick(Sender: TObject);
begin
DiagramInit;
end;

procedure TForm1.FormCreate(Sender: TObject);
begin
Diagram := false;
end;

procedure TForm1.YesClick(Sender: TObject);
var X, Y: Integer;
begin
  with Form1.Paintbox1.Canvas do begin
    Pen.Color:=ClBlack;
    Brush.Color:=ClRed;
    X:=3*ScrollBar1.Position+45-2;
    Y:=2*ScrollBar2.Position+15-2;
    Ellipse (X,Y,X+5,Y+5);
  end;
end;

end.
```

# 15

# Video Capture Cards

Fast and inexpensive PCI television cards are now readily available, therefore PC television is today a very common occurrence. A video picture contains a significant amount of information, which can also be utilised for technical measurements. Each colour video frame contains data for each pixel in the form of three colour intensities. The intensity values range from 0 to 255 for each of the three prime colours, red, green and blue (RGB). For full-screen video at $768 \times 568$ resolution, this means $3 \times 256 \times 768 \times 568 = 335,020,032$ bytes of information. Considering there are 25 frames each second in overlay mode, this information is available every 40 ms.

To gain maximum benefit from this chapter a PC video capture card must be installed. This need not necessarily be a television card; the following experiments use a WinTV Primio, but even a webcam with capture capabilities will work. Some capture cards support Windows Direct Draw because they impose significantly high demands on the PC graphics card. Specific requirements are specified by the card manufacturer. With a television card or capture card correctly installed it is simple to display and select a capture window using Windows API functions. Information can then be acquired from the selected window.

## 15.1 Picture Display

The AVICAP32.DLL is needed to generate a video picture window in a user program. This DLL is copied into the Windows System

*Listing 15.1*

*Windows DLL function call in Delphi*

directory during card installation, and it contains all the functions that are used in this chapter. The following code is written in Delphi 3. For creation of a new application, the code skeleton is imported and a single external call made to AVICAP32 using the function capCreateCaptureWindowA. This call creates a video capture window.

```
function     capCreateCaptureWindowA
   (lpName:pchar;
    dwStyle:DWORD;
    x,y,w,h,HWnd,nID:integer
    ):integer; stdcall; external 'AVICAP32.DLL';
```

*Listing 15.2*

*Constant declarations for the capture window*

To fix the required settings, communication with the capture window uses the Windows standard SendMessage call. The required constants are found in the header data of any C-developer environment, the most important of which have been translated into Pascal and then declared as constants.

```
implementation

{$R *.DFM}

const //from "AVICAP.H" Header File
WM_CAP_START                  =WM_USER;
WM_CAP_DRIVER_GET_CAPS         =(WM_CAP_START+  14);
WM_CAP_DRIVER_CONNECT          =(WM_CAP_START+  10);
WM_CAP_DRIVER_DISCONNECT       =(WM_CAP_START+  11);
WM_CAP_DLG_VIDEOFORMAT         =(WM_CAP_START+  41);
WM_CAP_DLG_VIDEOSOURCE         =(WM_CAP_START+  42);
WM_CAP_DLG_VIDEODISPLAY        =(WM_CAP_START+  43);
WM_CAP_GET_VIDEOFORMAT         =(WM_CAP_START+  44);
WM_CAP_SET_VIDEOFORMAT         =(WM_CAP_START+  45);
WM_CAP_DLG_VIDEOCOMPRESSION    =(WM_CAP_START+  46);
WM_CAP_SET_PREVIEW             =(WM_CAP_START+  50);
WM_CAP_SET_OVERLAY             =(WM_CAP_START+  51);
```

***continued on following page ...***

```
WM_CAP_SET_PREVIEWRATE              =(WM_CAP_START+   52);
WM_CAP_SET_SCALE                    =(WM_CAP_START+   53);
WM_CAP_GET_STATUS                   =(WM_CAP_START+   54);
WM_CAP_SET_SCROLL                   =(WM_CAP_START+   55);
WM_CAP_GRAB_FRAME                   =(WM_CAP_START+   60);
WM_CAP_GRAB_FRAME_NOSTOP            =(WM_CAP_START+   61);


VAR   cwnd: HWND;
```

Finally a window variable cwnd of type HWND is needed, which corresponds to an integer in Delphi 3. This is the window handle and is the first parameter in the SendMessage call.

On entry, the Delphi program must generate a capture window. This is done by placing the code into the OnCreate event of Form1, where the external function capCreateCaptureWindowA is invoked.

*Listing 15.3*
*Capture*
*window*
*creation*

```
procedure TForm1.FormCreate(Sender: TObject);

begin
  cwnd :=
  capCreateCaptureWindowA
  (nil,     // Title is invisible
   WS_CHILD + WS_VISIBLE + WS_OVERLAPPED,// style
   0,0, clientwidth, clientheight, handle,1);
  ShowWindow        (cwnd,SW_SHOW);
  SendMessage       (cwnd,WM_CAP_DRIVER_CONNECT,0,0);
  SendMessage       (cwnd,WM_CAP_SET_PREVIEWRATE,100,0);
  SendMessage       (cwnd, WM_CAP_SET_OVERLAY,1,0);
end;
```

The window title remains hidden due to the style selected. Size and position are set such that the window fits the full Form1 size parent rectangle. As the capture window is a child of Form1, the call handle parameter is the window handle of Form1. A call to the API function ShowWindow displays the capture window on the screen. Now the driver is connected to the capture window by sending the message DRIVER_CONNECT. To obtain an overlay

# 15 Video Capture Cards

**Figure 15.1**
*Capture window in a Delphi program*

**Listing 15.4**
*Releasing the driver*

mode display, the final call SET_OVERLAY is executed. These calls produce a picture in a video-window overlay, as shown in Figure 15.1.Once the application has ended, the driver must be released. This is done using the event OnClose on Form1 as follows:

```
procedure TForm1.FormClose(Sender: TObject; var Action: TCloseAction);
begin
   SendMessage (cwnd,WM_CAP_DRIVER_DISCONNECT,0,0);
end;
```

**Listing 15.5**
*Changing the window size*

A full-size video window is not always needed, so the window size can be changed. To always fit the capture window into the Form1 event OnSize is coded with the API call MoveWindow. Each time the form is sized, the capture window fits into the client area.

```
procedure TForm1.FormResize(Sender: TObject);
begin
   MoveWindow(cwnd,0,0,clientwidth,clientheight,false);
end;
```

Some properties of the capture window can be changed using suitable driver dialogues. The example program on the CD has a menu to call several option dialogues. Displaying a driver dialogue requires only one SendMessage call to the capture window with the appropriate constant. The dialogue itself is part of the capture card driver.

Some cards can be switched between different sources, such as television or external video. The WinTV Primio can be switched by calling the video source dialogue, as shown in Listing 15.6, which also allows the colour parameters to be modified.

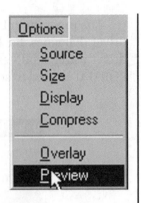

*Figure 15.2*

*Driver options of the compiled program*

*Listing 15.6*

*Starting the 'Video Source" dialogue*

```
procedure TForm1.Source1Click(Sender: TObject);
begin
  SendMessage (cwnd, WM_CAP_DLG_VIDEOSOURCE, 0, 0);
end;
```

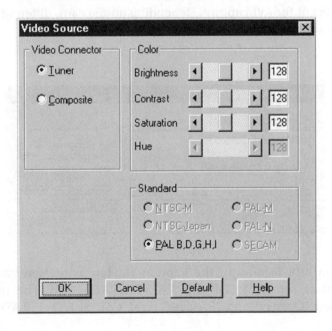

*Figure 15.3*

*Video Source driver dialogue*

The program in Listing 15.7 shows numerous further calls for driver dialogues. Each call sends the appropriate message to the driver using SendMessage. The message WM_CAP_DLG_VIDEO-FORMAT is used to set the video format size.

**Figure 15.4**

*Driver dialogue*
*for the*
*video format*

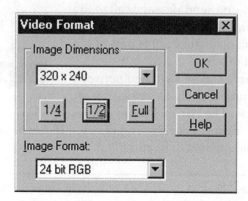

The dialogues 'Display' (WM_CAP_DLG_VIDEODISPLAY) and 'Compress' (WM_CAP_DLG_VIDEOCOMPRESSION) are only significant for AVI capture. Depending on the card, different dialogues are presented, and Figure 15.5 shows an example.

**Figure 15.5**

*Driver dialogue*
*for video*
*compression*

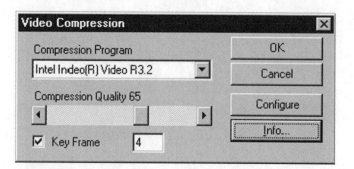

On initialisation of the capture window, a preview rate of 100ms is set (WM_CAP_SET_PREVIEWRATE, 100). The menu options 'Overlay' and 'Preview' (WM_CAP_SET_OVERLAY and

WM_CAP_SET_PREVIEW) can be used to switch modes. In preview mode a new picture is shown every 100 ms. Lower values
may work with high-performance CPU's and graphics cards.

*Listing 15.7*
*Full program for*
*displaying a*
*video window*

```
Unit1;

interface

uses
  Windows, Messages, SysUtils, Classes, Graphics,
  Controls, Forms, Dialogs, Menus;

Function    capCreateCaptureWindowA(lpName:pchar;dwStyle:DWORD;
x,y,w,h,HWnd,nID:integer):integer;
stdcall;external 'AVICAP32.DLL';

type
  TForm1 = class(TForm)
    MainMenu1: TMainMenu; File1: TMenuItem;
    End1: TMenuItem;  Edit1: TMenuItem;
    Source1: TMenuItem;   Gre1: TMenuItem;
    Display1: TMenuItem;  Compress1: TMenuItem;
    N1: TMenuItem;       Overlay1: TMenuItem;
    Preview1: TMenuItem;
    procedure FormCreate(Sender: TObject);
    procedure FormClose(Sender: TObject; var Action:
    TCloseAction);
    procedure FormResize(Sender: TObject);
    procedure End1Click(Sender: TObject);
    procedure Source1Click(Sender: TObject);
    procedure Gre1Click(Sender: TObject);
    procedure Display1Click(Sender: TObject);
    procedure Compress1Click(Sender: TObject);
    procedure Overlay1Click(Sender: TObject);
    procedure Preview1Click(Sender: TObject);
  end;

var
  Form1: TForm1;
```

*continued on following page ...*

```
implementation

{$R *.DFM}

const //From "AVICAP.H" Header-File
WM_CAP_START                        = WM_USER;
WM_CAP_DRIVER_GET_CAPS              =(WM_CAP_START+  14);
WM_CAP_DRIVER_CONNECT              =(WM_CAP_START+  10);
WM_CAP_DRIVER_DISCONNECT           =(WM_CAP_START+  11);
WM_CAP_DLG_VIDEOFORMAT             =(WM_CAP_START+  41);
WM_CAP_DLG_VIDEOSOURCE             =(WM_CAP_START+  42);
WM_CAP_DLG_VIDEODISPLAY            =(WM_CAP_START+  43);
WM_CAP_GET_VIDEOFORMAT             =(WM_CAP_START+  44);
WM_CAP_SET_VIDEOFORMAT             =(WM_CAP_START+  45);
WM_CAP_DLG_VIDEOCOMPRESSION        =(WM_CAP_START+  46);
WM_CAP_SET_PREVIEW                 =(WM_CAP_START+  50);
WM_CAP_SET_OVERLAY                 =(WM_CAP_START+  51);
WM_CAP_SET_PREVIEWRATE             =(WM_CAP_START+  52);
WM_CAP_SET_SCALE                   =(WM_CAP_START+  53);
WM_CAP_GET_STATUS                  =(WM_CAP_START+  54);
WM_CAP_SET_SCROLL                  =(WM_CAP_START+  55);
WM_CAP_GRAB_FRAME                  =(WM_CAP_START+  60);
WM_CAP_GRAB_FRAME_NOSTOP           =(WM_CAP_START+  61);
VAR  cwnd: HWND;

procedure TForm1.FormCreate(Sender: TObject);
begin
   cwnd :=
   capCreateCaptureWindowA
   ( nil, WS_CHILD + WS_VISIBLE +WS_OVERLAPPED,
     0,0, clientwidth, clientheight, handle, 1);
   ShowWindow   (cwnd,SW_SHOW);
   SendMessage (cwnd,WM_CAP_DRIVER_CONNECT,0,0);
   SendMessage (cwnd,WM_CAP_SET_PREVIEWRATE,100,0);
   SendMessage (cwnd, WM_CAP_SET_OVERLAY,1,0);
end;

procedure TForm1.FormClose(Sender: TObject;
     var Action: TCloseAction);
begin
   SendMessage (cwnd,WM_CAP_DRIVER_DISCONNECT, 0, 0);
end;
```

*continued on following page ...*

```
procedure TForm1.FormResize(Sender: TObject);
begin
    MoveWindow
    (cwnd,0,0,clientwidth,clientheight,false);
end;

procedure TForm1.End1Click(Sender: TObject);
begin
    close
end;

procedure TForm1.Source1Click(Sender: TObject);
begin
    SendMessage (cwnd, WM_CAP_DLG_VIDEOSOURCE, 0, 0);
end;

procedure TForm1.Gre1Click(Sender: TObject);
begin
    SendMessage (cwnd, WM_CAP_DLG_VIDEOFORMAT, 0, 0);
end;

procedure TForm1.Display1Click(Sender: TObject);
begin
    SendMessage (cwnd, WM_CAP_DLG_VIDEODISPLAY, 0, 0);
end;

procedure TForm1.Compress1Click(Sender: TObject);
begin
    SendMessage (cwnd, WM_CAP_DLG_VIDEOCOMPRESSION, 0, 0);
end;

procedure TForm1.Overlay1Click(Sender: TObject);
begin
    SendMessage (cwnd, WM_CAP_SET_OVERLAY, 1 , 0);
end;

procedure TForm1.Preview1Click(Sender: TObject);
begin
    SendMessage (cwnd, WM_CAP_SET_PREVIEW, 1 , 0);
end;

end.
```

## 15.2 Colour Information

In earlier sections a capture window was shown and to obtain the colour information from this window a device context is needed. The Windows device context (DC) is called canvas in Delphi. As the capture window is not a Delphi object, the methods and properties of Delphi objects fail. However, the Windows API calls which derived the Delphi objects will work.

Each standard window owns a Windows device context, and with a call to GetDC the handle of DC (hDC) can be read. At the end the DC must be released with ReleaseDC. Between both of these calls all the graphics operations can be executed.

The Win32 help file describes all the API functions needed to operate on a device context. To obtain the RGB value of a pixel, a call to the function GetPixel(hDC,x,y) is needed. The returned value is the colour word of the pixel as a 32-bit integer, i.e.:

    XXBBGGRR

*Listing 15.8*

*Separating the colour components*

The XX values are not relevant here, and to obtain the byte value of each colour from the Delphi code, the following basic operation can be used:

```
Color := GetPixel(hDC, x, y);
R:=Color                AND $FF;
G:=(Color SHR   8)      AND $FF;
B:=(Color SHR 16)       AND $FF;
```

With small alterations to the program shown in the previous section, RGB information can be continuously displayed in a status bar. To do this a Delphi StatusBar component is added to Form1. As the Client area of Form1 is decreased by this additional component, the procedure FormResize must be altered correspondingly. A 1ms timer is added and in the OnTimer event the RGB information of Pixel 0,0 is displayed in the status bar, as shown in figure 15.9.

```
procedure TForm1.FormResize(Sender: TObject);
begin
     MoveWindow(cwnd,0,0,clientwidth,clientheight -
          statusbar1.height,false);
end;

procedure TForm1.Timer1Timer(Sender: TObject);
var r,g,b,c,hdc:Integer;
begin
   hdc:=getdc(cwnd);
   c:=getpixel(hdc,0,0);
   releasedc(cwnd,hdc);
   r:=c and $FF;
   g:=(c shr  8) and $FF;
   b:=(c shr 16) and $FF;
   Statusbar1.simpletext:=
Format('RED:%03d GREEN:%03d BLUE:%03d',[r,g,b]);
end;
```

*Listing 15.9*

*Displaying colour information*

Colour values will change quickly with a moving image. When there is no signal on the display card, such as when no external source is connected or the signal is weak, a blue screen is displayed. In this case the status bar displays the colour values shown in Figure 15.6.

Red: 0 Green: 0 Blue: 200

*Figure 15.6*

*Colour values of a blue screen in the status bar*

## 15.3 Measuring length with a video camera

The program PalCapP on the CD is an experiment under Delphi 3 to measure length in an video image. The principle is simple and only needs the previously referenced functions. A 384 × 284 capture window is presented on the left, and its contents are copied into a bitmap for evaluation. The red, green, and blue values are graphically presented on the the right in the program window.

As an example, the width of a diskette can be determined. Two vertical lines separated by 10 mm (shown against the grid paper background) provide a length reference. This reference is detected by the red horizontal line and used to calculate the 'pixels per millimetre' factor. Using this, a reference a grid is drawn in the right window. The red reference line can be positioned with the left horizontal slider. The short dark lines in the graphic window also show the positions of the reference lines.

*Figure 15.7*
*Diskette width*
*measurement*

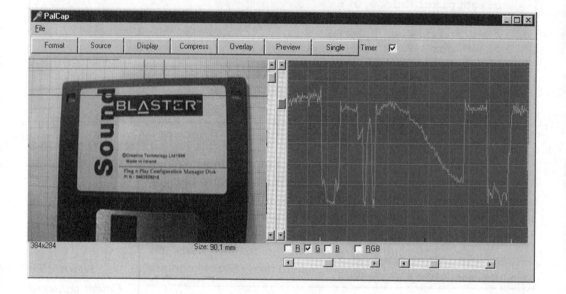

The screen on the right displays the green colour values of the picture line marked by the blue horizontal line in the capture window, with intensity increasing vertically. Due to the camera lens macro setting, the picture is somewhat distorted, nevertheless the length can still be accurately measured.

The program searches for a brightness threshold from the left and then from the right. Both thresholds can be adjusted using the two horizontal sliders. The threshold levels are indicated by small green markers at the bottom of the graphics window. The actual width in millimetres is calculated using the pixels per millimetre factor and the separation of the two levels.

Using this method only dark objects with high contrast can be measured. With a modified algorithm, other measurement procedures can also be implemented. For microscopic examination the reference lines used earlier are unsuitable, and a dark or light reference scale should be used instead.

# 16

# Asynchronous Serial Data Transmission

The original purpose of the RS232 interface is to provide asynchronous data transmission via the TxD and RxD lines. In contrast, most of the applications described in this book employ direct control via the auxiliary lines (DTR, RTS etc.) in order to realise low-cost control solutions, which amounts to bypassing the RS232 standard. This provides very inexpensive solutions, in particular for experimental applications, as compared with professional applications that are based on standardised serial connections between equipment.

Whilst clocked data transmission via the $I^2C$ bus or to a shift register works completely independently from a fixed transmission speed, asynchronous data transmission is dependent on an accurate baud rate that is the same for both parties. Data transmission can for example take place at 1200 bits per second (1200 baud), with each data byte prefaced by a start bit and terminated with a stop bit. Data transmission may be asynchronous, which means that it can start at any arbitrary time, because the start bit serves to synchronise the serial data receiver. All that is critical is that the same transmission parameters are set for the sender and the receiver.

## 16.1  Reading data from a serial mouse

Serial PC mice are operated from a COM interface, with the standard serial mouse obtaining its voltage supply from the RTS line. All mice events are transmitted to the PC as asynchronous, serial data stream. Even a mouse that has been retired from active service is still a complete interface which can be used for different tasks, such as interrogation of switch contacts and measurement of position, distance or speed.

Each movement of the mouse and each button push generates a mouse message. With a standard mouse, three bytes of information are generated regarding the buttons status and the relative movement in X and Y directions since the last message. The interface parameters are 1200 baud, 8 bits, no parity and two stop bits. If only one button is pressed, the mouse sends a complete message at the beginning and end of the click. The message has the following format:

Byte 1:

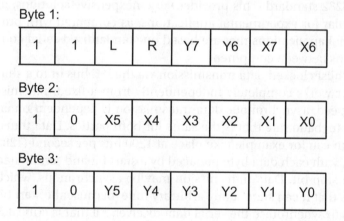

| 1 | 1 | L | R | Y7 | Y6 | X7 | X6 |

Byte 2:

| 1 | 0 | X5 | X4 | X3 | X2 | X1 | X0 |

Byte 3:

| 1 | 0 | Y5 | Y4 | Y3 | Y2 | Y1 | Y0 |

The 'Mouse' program below receives and evaluates all serial mouse data. The three received bytes are displayed unchanged initially. From the first byte the mouse button status is evaluated. The relative mouse co-ordinates dx and dy from bytes 2 and 3 and the most significant bits in Byte 1 are likewise displayed. Without

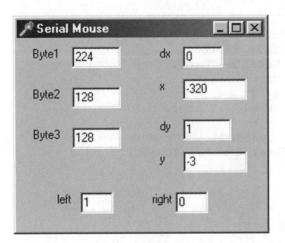

*Figure 16.1*
*Mouse data evaluation*

any mouse movement, null values are read, and with mouse movement it shows the direction, either positive or negative. Through summation, the absolute co-ordinates are integrated, such that the program presents absolute X and Y coordinates.

The serial data is received in a timer routine which strobes every 20 ms for new data. With each call the three bytes are read and processed. With a continuous movement a data bottleneck can occur in the serial receive buffer, such that with a distance measurement the evaluation can take longer than the actual mouse movement. This can result in a delayed display of results.

*Listing 16.1*
*Mouse data manipulation*

```
unit Mouse;

interface

uses PORTINC, Windows, Messages, SysUtils, Classes, Graphics,
   Controls, Forms, Dialogs, ExtCtrls, StdCtrls;

type
   TForm1 = class(TForm)
     Timer1: TTimer; Edit1: TEdit;
     Edit2: TEdit;   Edit3: TEdit;
     Edit4: TEdit;   Edit5: TEdit;
```

*continued on following page ...*

```
      Edit6: TEdit;   Edit7: TEdit;
      Edit8: TEdit;   Edit9: TEdit;
      Label1: TLabel;   Label2: TLabel;
      Label3: TLabel;   dx: TLabel;
      x: TLabel;   Label4: TLabel;
      Label5: TLabel;   Label6: TLabel;
      Label7: TLabel;
      procedure FormCreate(Sender: TObject);
      procedure Timer1Timer(Sender: TObject);
   end;

var
   Form1: TForm1;
   Din, Xtot, Ytot: Integer;

implementation

{$R *.DFM}

procedure TForm1.FormCreate(Sender: TObject);
begin
   OpenCom(pchar('com2:1200,N,8,2'));
   Timer1.Interval := 100;
   Timer1.Enabled := true;
   RTS(1);                    {power supply}
   Xges:=0; Yges:=0;
   Din := ReadByte;        {discard first byte}
end;

procedure TForm1.Timer1Timer(Sender: TObject);
var b1,b2,b3,x,y,li,re: Integer;
begin
   B1 := ReadByte;
   if B1=-1 then exit;
   Edit1.Text := FloatToStr(B1);
   B2 := ReadByte;
   Edit2.Text := FloatToStr(B2);
   B3 := ReadByte;
   Edit3.Text := FloatToStr(B2);
   x:= B2 And 63+64*(B1 and 3);
   if x> 128 then x:=x-256;
   y:= B3 And 63+16*(B1 and 12);
```

*continued on following page ...*

```
 if y> 128 then y:=y-256;
   Edit4.Text := FloatToStr(x);
   Edit5.Text := FloatToStr(y);
   li := (B1 and 32) div 32;
   re := (B1 and 16) div 16;
   Edit6.Text := FloatToStr(li);
   Edit7.Text := FloatToStr(re);
   Xges:=Xges+x;
   Yges:=Yges+y;
   Edit8.Text := FloatToStr(Xges);
   Edit9.Text := FloatToStr(Yges);
  end;

 end.
```

## 16.2  Digital control via RS232

Other than synchronous data transmission with data and a clock line, asynchronous data transmission is well suited for transmission over longer distances. Eventual time delays and pulses with slowly rising edges will not cause errors with the serial data transmission. For example, over the TxD line, one can communicate up to 50 metres with 1200 baud and a simple unshielded cable. On the other end of the line, serial data is converted to parallel data by a serial received with eight parallel output lines. With that it can in principle be used to control eight independent consumers. The serial receiver can be built purely electronically, with a UART (for example, the AY3-1015 or 6402) or with any desired microcontroller.

The serial send line TxD complements the serial receiver line RxD, and over a second line the status of eight digital inputs can be read in the opposite direction. The conversion of the parallel data into a serial data stream is performed with another circuit or a microcontroller.

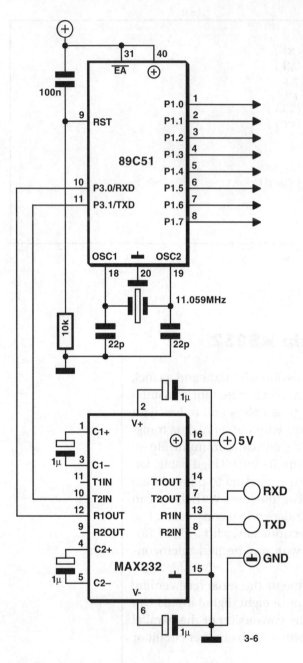

Here a solution using an 8051 controller is envisaged, there being numerous development boards with the 8051 / 8031 or their derivatives. A single-chip solution is also interesting, for example, an 89C51 flash controller in a 40-pin package or the smaller 89C2051 in a 20-pin DIL package. The microcontroller control program is mostly independent from type used and can thus generally be written in 8051 assembler. Figure 16.2 shows the typical format of an interface with an 89C51 controller. The serial interface uses a MAX232 for voltage level adaptation.

The program receives serial data and outputs it to Port P1. Each received byte is announced with a strobe pulse at P3.4. For every received byte, Port P1 status is read and returned. When working with a single-chip controller, P0 is still free for use of a complete input port and can be used with very small program changes.

When the program starts, the PC's serial interface must be opened with appropriate parameters. Here 9600 baud, no parity, eight data bits and one stop bit are used. The actual data transmission in each direction consists of using SendByte to send a data byte that is then received by ReadByte.

*Figure 16.2* Serial interface

```
;8051 Serial Interface      (COM51.ASM)
;11,059 MHz, 9600 Baud
#include 8051.H
        .org 0000H

START   mov     SP,#60H         ;set stack pointer
INIT    clr     TR1             ;Timer 1 stop
        mov     TH1,#0FAH       ;6 to overrun: 9600 Baud
        mov     TL1,#0FAH
        anl     TMOD,#0FH       ;Timer1: 8-bit auto-reload
        orl     TMOD,#20H
        setb    TR1             ;start Timer
        mov     SCON,#50H       ;Init RS232
        setb    TI
        orl     PCON,#80H       ;SMOD=1

NEXT    acall   RECV
        mov     P1,A            ;port output
        anl     P3,#0EFH        ;strobe pulse on P3.4
        orl     P3,#10H
        mov     A,P1            ;read port status
        acall   SEND
        sjmp    NEXT

RECV    jnb     RI,RECV
        mov     A,SBUF
        clr     RI
        ret

SEND    jnb     TI,SEND
        clr     TI
        mov     SBUF,A
        ret
        .end
```

*Listing 16.2*

*8051 assembler listing*

The interface used works with only one port for output and input. The 8051 ports are quasi-bi-directional ports similar to those seen with the PCF8574 (see Chapter 12.4); that is, they can be used as inputs with high-value pull-up resistors, if High state s are output previously. An unconnected port thus reads back the same state as what was sent out.

**Figure 16.3**
*8051 serial input and output*

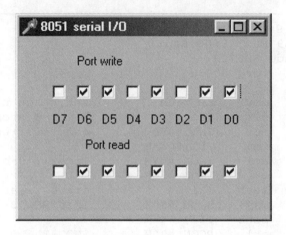

**Listing 16.3**

*Control with SendByte and ReadByte*

Program Port8051 provides eight checkboxes for both output and input. All outputs are transferred to the microcontroller at 100ms intervals, controlled by Timer 1. Input states are read and displayed at the same rate.

```
unit Port8051;

interface

uses PORTINC,Windows, Messages, SysUtils, Classes,
   Graphics, Controls, Forms, Dialogs, ExtCtrls, StdCtrls;

type
  TForm1 = class(TForm)
     CheckBox1: TCheckBox; CheckBox2: TCheckBox;
     CheckBox3: TCheckBox; CheckBox4: TCheckBox;
     CheckBox5: TCheckBox; CheckBox6: TCheckBox;
     CheckBox7: TCheckBox; CheckBox8: TCheckBox;
     Label1: TLabel; Label2: TLabel;
     Label3: TLabel; Label4: TLabel;
     Label5: TLabel; Label6: TLabel;
     Label7: TLabel; Label8: TLabel;
     Timer1: TTimer; Label9: TLabel;
     CheckBox9: TCheckBox; CheckBox10: TCheckBox;
     CheckBox11: TcheckBox; CheckBox12: TCheckBox;
     CheckBox13: TCheckBox; CheckBox14: TCheckBox;
     CheckBox15: TCheckBox; CheckBox16: TCheckBox;
```

***continued on following page ...***

```
    Label10: TLabel;
    procedure FormCreate(Sender: TObject);
    procedure Timer1Timer(Sender: TObject);
  end;

var
  Form1: TForm1;
  Dout, Din: Byte;

implementation

{$R *.DFM}

procedure TForm1.FormCreate(Sender: TObject);
begin
  OpenCOM (Pchar('COM2:9600,N,8,1'));
  Timer1.Interval := 100;
  Timer1.Enabled := true;
end;

procedure TForm1.Timer1Timer(Sender: TObject);
begin
  Dout := 0;
  if   CheckBox1.Checked Then Dout := Dout +1;
  if   CheckBox2.Checked Then Dout := Dout +2;
  if   CheckBox3.Checked Then Dout := Dout +4;
  if   CheckBox4.Checked Then Dout := Dout +8;
  if   CheckBox5.Checked Then Dout := Dout +16;
  if   CheckBox6.Checked Then Dout := Dout +32;
  if   CheckBox7.Checked Then Dout := Dout +64;
  if   CheckBox8.Checked Then Dout := Dout +128;
  SendByte (Dout);
  Delay (5);
  Din := ReadByte;
  CheckBox9.Checked  := ((Din And 1) >0);
  CheckBox10.Checked := ((Din And 2) >0);
  CheckBox11.Checked := ((Din And 4) >0);
  CheckBox12.Checked := ((Din And 8) >0);
  CheckBox13.Checked := ((Din And 16) >0);
  CheckBox14.Checked := ((Din And 32) >0);
  CheckBox15.Checked := ((Din And 64) >0);
  CheckBox16.Checked := ((Din And 128) >0);
 end;

end.
```

## 16.3 ST62 microcontroller UART

The ST62 family of small microcontrollers with internal EPROM from SGS offers several advantages, such as low power consumption, simple circuit designs and an internal A/D-converter. The circuit envisaged here (Reference [3]) uses an ST62E10 microcontroller as a universal serial interface. Via the serial interface a PC can control ten lines, either as digital outputs, digital inputs or analogue inputs. All ports are freely configurable. The microcontroller comes in a 20-pin DIL package and therefore needs only minimal external circuitry and around 2 mA to drive it. This programmable chip is available from *Elektor Electronics* (order number 7152). The somewhat larger ST62E15 in a 28-pin package offers eight additional I/O-lines. The program used here runs without modifications on both types.

The ST6 family of small CMOS microcontroller from SGS-Thompson features internal EPROM, an on chip 8-bit A/D converter and very versatile configurable I/O lines. The one-time programmable (OTP) version (in a plastic package with no UV window) offers a very favourable price/performance ratio.

All I/O lines can then be utilised for input or output, where a mixed use of ports is possible. Outputs can either then be configured as push pull outputs or open drain outputs, or as inputs with and without internal pull up resistors. From the 20 lines of the ST6215, 16 can then be used for analogue input. With the smaller ST6210 with collectively 12 I/O lines one has together eight analogue inputs. The internal A/D-converter has a resolution of 8 bits and needs a 5-V supply voltage as a reference voltage. All I/O actions are controlled over the processors control registers, which lie in the normal RAM area. Therefore, one needs only to provide external access to these registers, to utilise all advantages of the microcontrollers in an interface. Instead of using separate controller programs for each possible configuration, one needs only one program, which makes it possible to read and write all relevant RAM addresses of the ST6215. All further details are offloaded to the PC program layer to mitigate the processing burden on the microcontroller and maximise the joint throughput of the microcontroller and PC.

As there is no RS232 hardware in the chip, such as integrated into the 8051microcontroller, equivalent transmission routines must be programmed. Port line A0 serves as input RxD, and A1 is the output TxD. Figure 16.4 shows the complete circuit of the interface. The serial interface is designed entirely without a line driver. With the 4-MHz quartz crystal the baud rate is19,200 baud. If this is replaced by a 8-MHz crystal, the baud rate can be doubled.

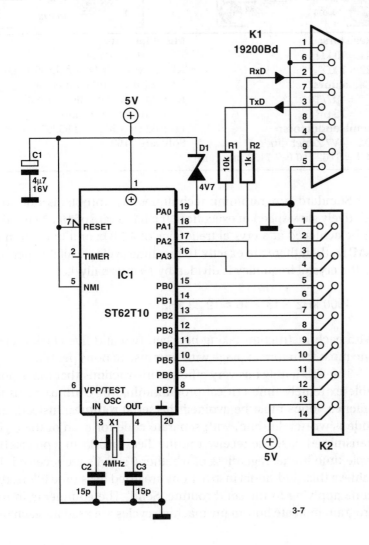

*Figure 16.4*

*Interface circuit*

**Figure 16.5**

*Component layout, circuit board layout and parts list for the interface*

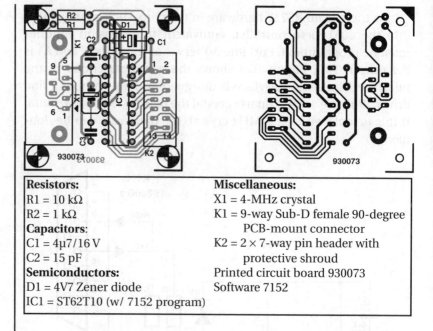

| Resistors: | Miscellaneous: |
|---|---|
| R1 = 10 kΩ | X1 = 4-MHz crystal |
| R2 = 1 kΩ | K1 = 9-way Sub-D female 90-degree |
| **Capacitors:** | PCB-mount connector |
| C1 = 4µ7/16 V | K2 = 2 × 7-way pin header with |
| C2 = 15 pF | protective shroud |
| **Semiconductors:** | Printed circuit board 930073 |
| D1 = 4V7 Zener diode | Software 7152 |
| IC1 = ST62T10 (w/ 7152 program) | |

Standard programming techniques face problems due to a relatively slow speed of execution. If a baud rate of 19,200 baud is to be achieved at a crystal frequency of 4 MHz or a maximum of 8 MHz, then there are exactly 16 machine cycles available per bit, as the crystal frequency is divided by 13 internally, i.e.:

$$4000 \text{ kHz} \div 13 \div 16 = 19.23 \text{ kHz}$$

With each instruction taking between two and five clock cycles, one must therefore manage with four instructions per bit.

The ST6 family has very efficient instructions that make possible extremely time-critical programming. In contrast to usual practice, loops must be avoided the serial routines. Instead, the code is written 'in-line', with separate code for each of the eight transmitted bits. The receive routine 'Recv' works in a precise 16-cycle time frame, regardless of whether 0's or 1's are received. To achieve this, additional instructions are fitted in as time fillers, the same applying to the send routine 'Send'. The comments in the program indicate how many machine cycles are used for each bit.

The main program is made up of one loop, in which data is received, interpreted and processed. With that the following scheme is consistent: when a register is to be read the PC sends a register address in the range 128 to 255; the controller then reads this address and sends the read byte back. In order to write to an address, bit 7 of the address must be reset. Accordingly, the address range is also shifted by 128 to the range of 0 to 127. Then the data byte is to be sent as the second byte. A very long waiting time between address and data byte leads to a reset that is generated by the watchdog timer of the ST6215.

*Listing 16.4*
*ST62E10/15*
*assembler*
*program*

```
    .title "RS232/19200 KB"
    .vers "st6215"
    .input "6215_reg.asm"

    .romsize 2
    .pp_on

dummy   .def 084H

    .section 1

    .org 80h
reset   ldi ddra,00000010B  ;A0 input RXD, no pull-up
        ldi ora, 00000010B  ;A1 output TXD P/P
        ldi dra, 00000001B  ;A2/3 inputs
        ldi ddrb,00000000B  ;B first inputs
        ldi orb, 00000000B
        ldi drb, 00000000B
        ldi ddrc,00000000B  ;C first inputs
        ldi orc, 00000000B
        ldi drc, 00000000B
        reti

    .org 600h   ;load high, so the OTP Version
            ;with lower address can also be programmed

mainlp ldi wdr,0FEH      ;reset watchdog
       jrr  0,dra,mainlp ;wait for start bit
       call Recv2        ;RS232 receiver after start bit  11
       jrs  7,a,read     ;>= 128: read register          +5
```

**continued on following page . . .**

```
write    addi a,128        ;instruction 1: register write  +4
         ld   x,a          ;register address               +4
         call Recv         ;data                         +4 = 28
         ld   (x),a        ;write to register             11+4
         jp mainlp         ;                             +4 = 22
read     ld   x,a          ;register address
         ld   a,(x)        ;read
         call Send         ;send back
         jp   mainlp

Recv     jrr  0,dra,Recv   ;Rs232 RXD=A0, 19,2k / 4MHz 5..10
         ldi  dummy,0      ;4
Recv2    ldi  a,0          ;4   jump here after start bit
         ldi  dummy,0      ;4
         nop               ;2 : 21 to 27 after start bit
data0    jrs  0,dra,wait0  ;5
         addi a,1          ;4
         jrnc data1        ;2
wait0    addi a,0
         nop
data1    jrs  0,dummy,data1 ;5  16/bit
         jrs  0,dra,wait1  ;5
         addi a,2          ;4
         jrnc data2        ;2
wait1    addi a,0
         nop
data2    jrs  0,dummy,data2 ;5  16/bit
         jrs  0,dra,wait2  ;5
         addi a,4          ;4
         jrnc data3        ;2
wait2    addi a,0
         nop
data3    jrs  0,dummy,data3 ;5  16/bit
         jrs  0,dra,wait3  ;5
         addi a,8          ;4
         jrnc data4        ;2
wait3    addi a,0
         nop
data4    jrs  0,dummy,data4 ;5  16/bit
         jrs  0,dra,wait4  ;5
         addi a,16         ;4
         jrnc data5        ;2
wait4    addi a,0
         nop
```

*continued on following page . . .*

```
data5   jrs   0,dummy,data5  ;5   16/bit
        jrs   0,dra,wait5    ;5
        addi  a,32           ;4
        jrnc  data6          ;2
wait5   addi  a,0
        nop
data6   jrs   0,dummy,data6  ;5   16/bit
        jrs   0,dra,wait6    ;5
        addi  a,64           ;4
        jrnc  data7          ;2
wait6   addi  a,0
        nop
data7   jrs   0,dummy,data7  ;5   16/bit
        jrs   0,dra,wait7    ;5
        addi  a,128          ;4
wait7   ret                  ;2   11, stop bit free

;RS232 Send with 19200 Baud/4MHz, TXD=A1
Send    ldi   dummy,0        ;4
        ldi   dra,00000011B  ;Start bit
        nop                  ;2
        jrr   0,dummy,bit1   ;5
bit1    jrs   0,a,s10        ;5
        ldi   dra,00000011B  ;4   16/bit
        jrnc  s0             ;2
s10     ldi   dra,00000001B
        nop
s0      jrs   0,dummy,s0     ;5
        jrs   1,a,s11        ;5
        ldi   dra,00000011B  ;4   16/bit
        jrnc  s1             ;2
s11     ldi   dra,00000001B
        nop
s1      jrs   0,dummy,s1     ;5
        jrs   2,a,s21        ;5
        ldi   dra,00000011B  ;4
        jrnc  s2             ;2
s21     ldi   dra,00000001B
        nop
s2      jrs   0,dummy,s2     ;5
        jrs   3,a,s31        ;5
        ldi   dra,00000011B  ;4
        jrnc  s3             ;2
s31     ldi   dra,00000001B
        nop
```

*continued on following page ...*

```
s3      jrs  0,dummy,s3     ;5
        jrs  4,a,s41        ;5
        ldi  dra,00000011B  ;4
        jrnc s4             ;2
s41     ldi  dra,00000001B
        nop
s4      jrs  0,dummy,s4     ;5
        jrs  5,a,s51        ;5
        ldi  dra,00000011B  ;4
        jrnc s5             ;2
s51     ldi  dra,00000001B
        nop
s5      jrs  0,dummy,s5     ;5
        jrs  6,a,s61        ;5
        ldi  dra,00000011B  ;4
        jrnc s6             ;2
s61     ldi  dra,00000001B
        nop
s6      jrs  0,dummy,s6     ;5
        jrs  7,a,s71        ;5
        ldi  dra,00000011B  ;4
        jrnc s7             ;2
s71     ldi  dra,00000001B
        nop
s7      nop                 ;2
        nop                 ;2
        nop                 ;2
        nop                 ;2
        nop                 ;2  16/bit
        ldi  dra,00000001B  ;stop bit
        ret

        .section 32
        .org 00h
adc     nop
        reti
timer   nop
        reti
int2    nop
        reti
int1    nop
        reti
        .org 0ch
nmi     nop
        reti
res     jp reset
```

The interface utilisation is only possible with the knowledge of register functions of this microcontroller. The I/O line properties are controlled via the three registers *ddr* (direction register), *or* (option register) and *dr* (data register), which exist threefold, i.e. for the Ports A, B and C. The following table shows the most important settings. Each line of the Ports can be fully independently configured.

| ddr | or | dr | Function |
|-----|----|----|----------|
| 0 | 0 | 0 | input with pull-up resistor |
| 0 | 0 | 1 | input without pull-up |
| 0 | 1 | 1 | analogue input, not for PA0–3 & PC0–3 |
| 1 | 0 | x | open-drain output |
| 1 | 1 | x | push-pull output |

The following Delphi program demonstrates the use of the interface. For digital I/O, firstly the type of port line must be configured. Then data can be exchanged concurrently with the corresponding data registers of the corresponding ports.

The A/D converter is used by firstly selecting a line as an input via the port register. The actual conversion is started over the A/D control register. As the conversion only needs some 140 µsec, the result can be read without delay from the A/D data register.

The example program uses all Port lines of the controller PA2 and PA3 were then initialised as digital inputs with pull up resistance, so that one, for example can use a switch between connected to earth. Note that port PA0 (TxD) and PA1 (RxD) must retain their old settings as can be seen from the assembler listing.

Port B was divided and PB0 to PB3 were used as digital push pull outputs. They are of low resistance even in the high state and can directly drive ULN2803 Darlington drivers. The upper four lines PB3 to PB7 were then initialised as high resistance digital inputs without Pull ups. Concurrently, all analogue inputs are read via the AD converter. In this manner four digital inputs are obtained as well as four analogue channels with a resolution of eight bits.

**Figure 16.6**

*Access to all port lines*

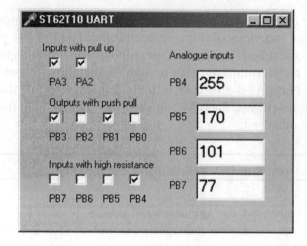

**Listing 16.5**

*Direct control of port pins*

```
unit ST62;

interface

uses PORTINC, Windows, Messages, SysUtils, Classes,
   Graphics, Controls, Forms, Dialogs, StdCtrls, ExtCtrls;

type
   TForm1 = class(TForm)
      Splitter1: TSplitter;
      CheckBox1: TCheckBox; CheckBox2: TCheckBox;
      Label1: TLabel; Label2: TLabel;
      Label3: TLabel; Label4: TLabel;
      CheckBox3: TCheckBox; CheckBox4: TCheckBox;
      CheckBox5: TCheckBox; CheckBox6: TCheckBox;
      Label5: TLabel; Label6: TLabel;
      Label7: TLabel; Label8: TLabel;
      Label9: TLabel; Label10: TLabel;
      CheckBox7: TCheckBox; CheckBox8: TCheckBox;
      CheckBox9: TCheckBox; CheckBox10: TCheckBox;
      Label11: TLabel; Label12: TLabel;
      Label13: TLabel; Label14: TLabel;
      Edit1: TEdit; Edit2: TEdit;
      Edit3: TEdit; Edit4: TEdit;
```

***continued on following page . . .***

```
      Label15: TLabel; Label16: TLabel;
      Label17: TLabel; Label18: TLabel;
      Timer1: TTimer;
      procedure FormCreate(Sender: TObject);
      procedure Timer1Timer(Sender: TObject);
   end;

var
   Form1: TForm1;

implementation

{$R *.DFM}

const ddra = $C4;                        { direction register a-c }
      ddrb = $C5;
      ddrc = $C6;
      ora  = $CC;                        { option register a-c }
      orb  = $CD;
      orc  = $CE;
      dra  = $C0;                        { data register a-c }
      drb  = $C1;
      drc  = $C2;
      adcr = $D1;                        { A/D control register }
      adr  = $D0;                        { A/D data register }
procedure RegOut (Address, Data : Byte);
begin
   SendByte (Address AND 127);
   SendByte (Data);
end;

function RegIn (Address : Byte): Byte;
begin
   SendByte (Address);
   Regin := ReadByte;
end;

function Analogue: Integer;
begin
   RegOut (adcr,$30);                    { start measurement }
   Analogue := (RegIn (adr));            { read measurement }
end;
```

*continued on following page ...*

```
procedure TForm1.FormCreate(Sender: TObject);
begin
  OpenCOM (Pchar('COM2:19200,N,8,1'));
  Timer1.Interval := 100;
  Timer1.Enabled := true;
  RegOut (ddra,$02);               { Port A divided }
  RegOut (ora,$02);                { PA2,3 input w/ pullup }
  RegOut (dra,$01);                { PA0 output, PA1 input }
  RegOut (ddrb,$0F);               { Port B divided }
  RegOut (orb,$0F);                { PB0-3 outputs }
  RegOut (drb,$10);                { PB4-7 inputs }
end;

procedure TForm1.Timer1Timer(Sender: TObject);
var Dout, Din1, Din2: Integer;
begin
  Din1 := RegIn (dra);                {PA read}
  CheckBox1.Checked := ((Din1 and 4)=4);
  CheckBox2.Checked := ((Din1 and 8)=8);
  Dout := 0;
  if CheckBox3.Checked then Dout := Dout + 1;
  if CheckBox4.Checked then Dout := Dout + 2;
  if CheckBox5.Checked then Dout := Dout + 4;
  if CheckBox6.Checked then Dout := Dout + 8;
  Dout := Dout OR $F0;
  RegOut (drb,Dout);
  RegOut (orb, RegIn (orb) AND $0F); {PB4-7 Inputs}
  Din2 := RegIn (drb);                {PB4 read}
  CheckBox7.Checked := ((Din2 and 16)=16);
  CheckBox8.Checked := ((Din2 and 32)=32);
  CheckBox9.Checked := ((Din2 and 64)=64);
  CheckBox10.Checked := ((Din2 and 128)=128);
  RegOut (orb, $1F);                  {PB4 analogue input}
  Edit1.Text := FloatToStr (Analogue);
  RegOut (orb, $2F);                  {PB5 analogue input}
  Edit2.Text := FloatToStr (Analogue);
  RegOut (orb, $4F);                  {PB6 analogue input}
  Edit3.Text := FloatToStr (Analogue);
  RegOut (orb, $8F);                  {PB7 analogue input}
  Edit4.Text := FloatToStr (Analogue);
end;

end.
```

The programming example above shows only one of the many possible configurations of the interface. It is very versatile as ten freely configurable port pins can be used arbitrarily. Ten digital outputs could be configures for example, whereby two more pins stay free as digital inputs or outputs. If the program is used with the larger ST6215, then there are even 20 port lines available.

## 16.4  A serial bus

Many interfaces operate at the serial interface. A drawback with this is that sometimes in the normal case only one device can be used with one line, other than for example with the SCSI bus. Often it is however desirable to cascade interfaces to a bus system. It is the aim of the design introduced here to be able to use up to 16 interfaces in one line (Reference [4]).

All 8051 microcontrollers have an optional 9-bit mode for the internal UART. The ninth bit can, for example, be set as a parity bit. But it can also be used for a special multi-processor mode. In this mode, bytes are only received if the ninth bit is set. This was intended for transmission of an address. Each connected micro-controller receives and compares the address with an internal constant. Only the addressed processor will then reply, where-upon all the further communication is performed with bit 9 low, that is in single-processor mode.

For communication between several 8051 controllers, this technique is generally known but not very often used . In princi-pal the PC serial interface also has a ninth data bit, which is used as a parity bit. When a serial interface is opened, the parity bits can be specified. Besides none (N), even (E) and odd (O) parity, a constant 1 bit (mark, M) or 0 bit (space, S) can be chosen. 'Mark' corresponds to the Multi-Processor mode, and 'space' to the Single-Processor mode.

The electrical properties of the RS232 interface were not designed for bus operation, but in principle it is possible to use it for this. The TxD line of PC's can without any problems drive sev-eral receivers, especially if they use rather high resistance inputs. For the RxD line a wired-OR connection must be chosen. The sig-

**Figure 16.7**

*Bus interface*

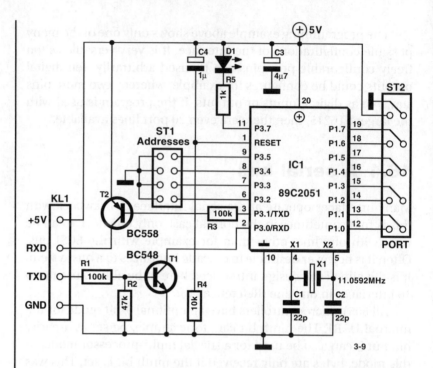

nal of more interfaces were with that, for example combined over diodes. When always only one device transmits at any one time then there can be no bus conflict. This method can be used with any 8051 system. Here however a small interface was introduced with an 89C2051.

The circuit picture in Figure 16.7 shows a simple one chip system with an RS232 interface with transistors. The input (TxD from PC) is of high resistance. The output (RxD to PC) works with an open PNP collector, so that the postulated OR connection results for several systems. The interface permits 16 different addresses to be selected using Jumpers. The addressed status is displayed over an LED. Here one port (P1) is available as a connection to the outside world.

The software also permits limited access to port 3. With that it is possible, for example to directly switch the LED, interrogate the internal comparator of the 89C2051 or use the address jumper lines as additional inputs.

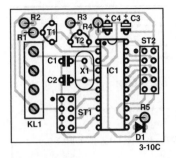
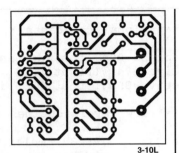

3-10C          3-10L

*Figure 16.8*

*Component
layout, circuit
board layout
and parts list
for the bus
interface*

| Resistors: | Semiconductors: |
|---|---|
| R1, R3 = 100 kΩ | D1 = LED |
| R2 = 47 kΩ | T1 = BC548 |
| R4 = 10 kΩ | T2 = BC558 |
| R5 = 1 kΩ | IC1 = 89C2051 |
| **Capacitors:** | **Miscellaneous:** |
| C1, C2 = 22 pF | X1 = 11.0592 MHz crystal |
| C3 = 4µ7/16 V | KL1 = 4-way screw terminal, PCB-mount |
| C4 = 1 µF/16 V | ST1 = 2 × 4-way pin header |
|  | ST32 = 2 × 5-way pin header |

The 89C2051 internal control program was developed with
the MC macro compiler of the ES51 development system. A free
trial version of the MC2051 macro compiler, specifically for the
89C2051, is on the CD. It can also be used without the development system, for example to adapt the software. The output file is
generated as a binary file that can be directly burned in the
processor. In principle though it also not difficult to write the program in assembly language. MC was however employed, because
it helps with a very effective development.

*Listing 16.6
Controller
program
in MC*

```
;Multi Interface Bus for 8051/89C2052
;(C) 1997 B. Kainka
;
;Compiled by Macro Compiler MC
;development tool: ES51-board by Module-Bus
;www.modul-bus.de)
```

**continued on following page ...**

```
;************** global constants ******************

define base_address 00h ;bus addresses 00h to 0Fh
define bus_active B7h  ;LED at P3.7
;define bus_active B5h ;LED at P3.5 in EPROM systems


;************** low level routines *****************

Procedure Init            ;RS232, multi processor + delay timer
Define RI    98h          ;SCON.0
Define TI    99h          ;SCON.1
WrTH1   FAH               ;divide by 6, 9600 Baud
WrTL1   FAH
WrTH0   252               ;divide by 942 : 1ms
WrTL0   122
WrTMOD   00100001b        ;timer1: 8 bit auto reload, t0 16 Bit
WrTCON   01010000b        ;start timer 0 and 1
WrSCON   11111010b        ;init RS232: mode 3,
                          ;multi processor, TB8=1
WrPCON   10000000b        ;80H, SMOD=1
EndProc


Procedure RdCOM
WhileNotBit RI            ;loop until RI=1
EndWhile
ClearBit    RI           ;RI := 0
RdSBUF                    ;read byte
EndProc
Procedure WrCOM
WhileNotBit TI            ;loop until TI=1
EndWhile
WrSBUF                    ;send byte
EndProc


Procedure Delay           ;0...255ms
   Define TF0   8Dh       ;TCON.5
   Define TR0   8Ch       ;TCON.4
   Define TH0   8Ch       ;high byte
   Define TL0   8Ah       ;low byte
WhileA>0
   WhileNotBit TF0
   EndWhile
   ClearBit    TR0        ;Timer0 stop
   ClearBit    TF0
```

*continued on following page ...*

```
   MovAdr TH0   252       ;divide by 922: 1ms
   MovAdr TL0   112
   SetBit TR0             ;Timer0 start
   A-1
EndWhile
EndProc


;***************** bus routines ********************

Procedure output_P1
RdCOM                     ;read data byte
WrP1                      ;write to port 1
A 255                     ;remain in address mode
EndProc


Procedure output_P3
RdCOM                     ;read data byte
OR 00000011b              ;P3.0, P3.1 remain set
WrP3                      ;write to port 3
A 255                     ;remain in address mode
EndProc


Procedure input_P1
RdP1                      ;read port 1
WrCOM                     ;send byte
A 255                     ;remain in address mode
EndProc


Procedure input_P3
RdP3                      ;read port 3
WrCOM                     ;send byte
A 255                     ;remain in address mode
EndProc


Procedure input2
RdP3                      ;read port 3
WrCOM                     ;send byte
A 255                     ;remain in address mode
EndProc


Procedure outputs
RdMem 1                   ;received command
IfA= 16 output_P1
IfA= 17 output_P3
EndProc
```

*continued on following page . . .*

```
Procedure inputs
RdMem 1                 ;received command
IfA= 32 input_P1
IfA= 33 input_P3
EndProc

Procedure Interpreter
RdMem 2                 ;read device address
WrCOM                   ;return address
ClearBit bus_active     ;LED on
WrSCON 11010010b        ;SM2=0 single processor, bit8 = 0, TB8=0
WhileA>0
   RdCOM                ;read command
   WrMem 1              ;save command
   AND 11110000b        ;
   IfA= 16 outputs
   IfA= 32 inputs
;   IfA= 48 ADC
EndWhile
WrSCON  11111010b       ;InitRS232 SM2=1, TB8=1
SetBit bus_active       ;LED off
EndProc

Procedure watch_address_byte
RdMem 2
WrB
RdCOM
IfA=B Interpreter       ;InitRS232 SM2=0   (addressed)
EndProc

Begin
Init
RdP3                    ;read hardware address
NOT
AND 00111100b           ;only P3.2 ...P3.5
ShiftRight
ShiftRight
+ base_address          ;add software coded address
WrMem 2                 ;save device address
Loop watch_address_byte
End
```

When started, the program first reads the selected bus address. It then monitors the serial interface in multi-processor mode to see if its own address has appeared. When that is the case, the controller answers with its address and switches the LED on. Then the single-processor mode is enabled and a definitive interface protocol is activated. It is valid for the following commands:

| | |
|---|---|
| 16 | Output Port 1 |
| 17 | Output Port 3 |
| 32 | Read Port 1 |
| 33 | Read Port 3 |
| 0–15 | Disconnect from bus |

The protocol can incidentally be directly tested with MC2051. The program has a simple terminal for transmission of single bytes. The parity bit can be switched directly from this terminal when M is pressed (Mark, address mode) or S (Space, data mode).

The commands are ordered in groups of 16, so that one can easily build further functions. If for example, an A/D-converter with more channels is to be used, then the commands from 48 onwards can be used for the individual channel selection. This expansion is hinted in the listing but it depends on the controller which is used.

There is an interesting alternative for addressing this chip. There is a fixed base address in the program, which is intended to be used if more than 16 systems are to be adopted in a second version of the controller. Also, a completely fixed address can be used in the software without any jumpers. In this manner, four more port pins can be utilised for other jobs. All these extensions can be made without too much learning time by using the compiler on the CD.

A simple test can show, which addresses on the bus correspond with which interface. A programs sends thereby in address mode, that is with parity bit (Mark parity) all possible addresses and evaluates the answer of interfaces. Each addressed interface answers with its address. The following program searches through the range from 1 to 10. It shows two connected bus participants, whose addresses are set to 2 and 8. During the test a brief flashing

**Figure 16.9**
*Bus test with two occupied bus addresses*

**Listing 16.7**
*Search for active bus addresses*

of the LED will be seen when an interface is addressed. Every interface disconnects when the next device is addressed. The test program can operate permanently in address mode, as no further data transmission is intended.

```
unit Bustest;

interface

uses PORTINC, Windows, Messages, SysUtils, Classes,
  Graphics, Controls, Forms, Dialogs, StdCtrls;

type
  TForm1 = class(TForm)
    CheckBox1: TCheckBox;    CheckBox2: TCheckBox;
    CheckBox3: TCheckBox;    CheckBox4: TCheckBox;
    CheckBox5: TCheckBox;    CheckBox6: TCheckBox;
    CheckBox7: TCheckBox;    CheckBox8: TCheckBox;
    CheckBox9: TCheckBox;    CheckBox10: TCheckBox;
    Button1: TButton;
```
***continued on following page . . .***

```
    procedure FormCreate(Sender: TObject);
    procedure Button1Click(Sender: TObject);
  end;

var
  Form1: TForm1;

implementation

{$R *.DFM}

procedure TForm1.FormCreate(Sender: TObject);
begin
  OpenCOM (Pchar('COM2:9600,M,8,1')); {Address mode}
end;

procedure TForm1.Button1Click(Sender: TObject);
begin
  SendByte (1);
  CheckBox1.Checked := (ReadByte = 1);
  SendByte (2);
  CheckBox2.Checked := (ReadByte = 2);
  SendByte (3);
  CheckBox3.Checked := (ReadByte = 3);
  SendByte (4);
  CheckBox4.Checked := (ReadByte = 4);
  SendByte (5);
  CheckBox5.Checked := (ReadByte = 5);
  SendByte (6);
  CheckBox6.Checked := (ReadByte = 6);
  SendByte (7);
  CheckBox7.Checked := (ReadByte = 7);
  SendByte (8);
  CheckBox8.Checked := (ReadByte = 8);
  SendByte (9);
  CheckBox9.Checked := (ReadByte = 9);
  SendByte (10);
  CheckBox10.Checked := (ReadByte = 10);
end;

end.
```

In order to perform real accesses to single bus participants it is necessary to switch between address mode and data mode alternately. This can be done using the OpenCOM function, where the parity bit is changed accordingly. Before opening the interface it must be closed first by CloseCOM. The program shown in Listing 16.8 transmits data to the ports of two devices with bus addresses 2 and 8. The output data can be set by slider controls and can for example be used to drive a D/A converter connected to the interface.

*Figure 16.10*

*Outputs on two bus addresses*

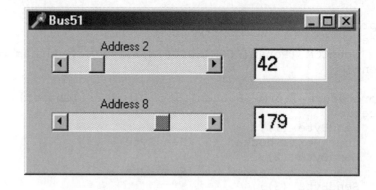

*Listing 16.8*

*Port output via two interfaces*

```
unit BusOut;

interface

uses PORTINC, Windows, Messages, SysUtils, Classes,
   Graphics, Controls, Forms, Dialogs, ExtCtrls, StdCtrls;

type
   TForm1 = class(TForm)
      ScrollBar1: TScrollBar;   Edit1: TEdit;
      ScrollBar2: TScrollBar;   Edit2: TEdit;
      Label1: TLabel;   Label2: TLabel;
      Timer1: TTimer;
      procedure Timer1Timer(Sender: TObject);
   end;
```

*continued on following page . . .*

```
var
  Form1: TForm1;

implementation

{$R *.DFM}

procedure Output (Address, Data: Integer);
var dummy: Integer;
begin
  OpenCOM (Pchar('COM2:9600,M,8,1'))      ; {Address mode}
  SendByte (Address);
  Dummy := ReadByte;
  CloseCOM;
  OpenCOM (Pchar('COM2:9600,S,8,1'))      ; {Data mode}
  SendByte (16)                           ; {Output}
  SendByte (Data);
  SendByte (0);                           ; {Disconnected}
  CloseCOM;
end;

procedure TForm1.Timer1Timer(Sender: TObject);
begin
  Output (2,ScrollBar1.Position);
  Edit1.Text := FloatToStr (ScrollBar1.Position);
  Output (8,ScrollBar2.Position);
  Edit2.Text := FloatToStr (ScrollBar2.Position);
end;

end.
```

Switching between address and data mode is rather slow when closing and opening the COM interface. If a very fast switching is needed the COM interface can be reprogrammed by directly writing to the UART registers. This will change the parity setting behind the back of Windows by using direct port access. The following example demonstrates this fast switching with a running-light display. Altogether 16 lamps are to be controlled by two devices that use bus addresses 2 and 8. The output of two bytes is performed by the procedure OUTPUT16, where low bytes and high bytes are output to different bus addresses.

Faster switching with ADDRESSMODE and DATAMODE uses direct register programming of the COM interface.

One must respect here, that the COM port address must align with the COM port opened by OpenCOM (COM2 in this case). This type of the switching succeeds under Windows 95/98, but is no longer possible under Windows NT.

*Figure 16.11*

*Running-light display control*

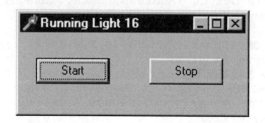

*Listing 16.9*

*Fast bus output for a 16-bit running light*

```
unit BusRun;

interface

uses PORTINC, Windows, Messages, SysUtils, Classes,
   Graphics, Controls, Forms, Dialogs, ExtCtrls, StdCtrls;

type
  TForm1 = class(TForm)
Start: TButton;   Stop: TButton;
Timer1: TTimer;
procedure FormCreate(Sender: TObject);
procedure Timer1Timer(Sender: TObject);
procedure StartClick(Sender: TObject);
procedure StopClick(Sender: TObject);
  end;

var
  Form1: TForm1;

implementation
```

*continued on following page . . .*

```
{$R *.DFM}

const COM1 : Integer = $03F8;
COM2 : Integer = $02F8;
COM3 : Integer = $03E8;
COM4 : Integer = $02E8;
var Pattern: Word;

procedure AddressMode;
begin
   OutPort(COM2+3,$2B);              { 8-Bit, 1-Parity, 1 Stopbit }
end;

procedure DataMode;
begin
   OutPort(COM2+3,$3B);              { 8-Bit, 0-Parity, 1 Stopbit }
end;

procedure Output16(Data:Word);
var Dummy: Integer;
begin
   AddressMode;
   SendByte(2);
   Dummy := ReadByte;
   DataMode;
   SendByte (16);
   SendByte (lo(Data));
   SendByte (0);
   AddressMode;
   SendByte(8);
   Dummy := ReadByte;
   DataMode;
   SendByte (16);
   SendByte (hi(Data));
   SendByte (0);
end;

procedure TForm1.FormCreate(Sender: TObject);
begin
   OpenCOM (Pchar('COM2:9600,M,8,1'));        {Adressmodus}
   Pattern := 1;
end;
```

*continued on following page ...*

```
procedure TForm1.Timer1Timer(Sender: TObject);
begin
   OutPut16(Pattern);
   Pattern := Pattern * 2;
   If Pattern = 0 then Pattern := 1;
end;

procedure TForm1.StartClick(Sender: TObject);
begin
   Timer1.Enabled := true;
end;

procedure TForm1.StopClick(Sender: TObject);
begin
   Timer1.Enabled := false;
end;

end.
```

When a program only needs read access to the processor ports, it is unnecessary to switch to the data mode. If one stays entirely in address mode, then the read command 32 will be also received and interpreted as an address by any bus participant that is not addressed at this moment. But as there are only bus addresses up to 15, in fact no other system will be addressed. So only the active system will answer the port request.

Every system which is addressed will quit from the bus, if any different bus address in the range of 0 to 15 is recognised. Disconnecting a system can therefore be achieved by sending a byte 0. This simplified control in address mode only, can only be used for read accesses. It would be possible for write access only if data bytes below 16 are never needed, as they would be misunderstood as addresses. This is possible by only using seven bits with outputs and leaving the highest bit set.

The following program shows the simplified control in Visual Basic. With readout of Ports P1 on the AT89C2051 one must respect, that pins P1.0 and P1.2 have no internal pull-ups but are of high resistance. They serve at the same time as analogue inputs for the internal comparator. The comparator can be read with read command 33 with a read access to Port 3. Port bit P3.6 is not connected to a pin of the AT89C2051 but to the internal comparator output.

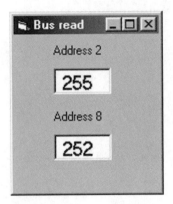

*Figure 16.12*
*Port data*
*readout*

*Listing 16.10*
*Port readout*
*via the bus*

```
Private Sub Form_Load()
  i = OPENCOM("COM2,9600,M,8,1")    'Address mode
  If i = 0 Then MsgBox ("COM2 unavailable")
End Sub

Private Sub Form_Unload(Cancel As Integer)
   CLOSECOM
End Sub

Private Sub Timer1_Timer()
   SENDBYTE (2)
   Dummy = READBYTE
   SENDBYTE (32)
   Data = READBYTE
   Text1.Text = Str$(Data)
   SENDBYTE (8)
   Dummy = READBYTE
   SENDBYTE (32)
   Data = READBYTE
   Text2.Text = Str$(Data)
End Sub
```

# Appendix

## References

[1]  B.Kainka, *PC-Schnittstellen Angewandt*, Elektor-Verlag, 6th edition, 1997

[2]  Philips, PCF8574 and PCF8591 data sheets

[3]  B.Kainka, 'Microcontroller UART', Elektor Electronics 5/94, p 16

[4]  B.Kainka, 'The Ninth Bit', 1997/98 Microcontroller Competition , Elektor Electronics CD-ROM 1998

# Appendix

# Index

## IC components

| | |
|---|---|
| 16450 | 34 |
| 27128 | 154 |
| 27256 | 154 |
| 2764 | 154 |
| 4011 | 122 |
| 4021 | 106 |
| 4094 | 99 |
| 558 | 199 |
| 8051 | 252, 267 |
| 8243 | 145 |
| 8250 | 34 |
| 8255 | 10 |
| 89C2051 | 252, 268 |
| 89C51 | 252 |
| AD654 | 90 |
| LM324 | 72 |
| MAX232 | 252 |
| PCF8574 | 170 |
| PCF8591 | 177 |
| S201–D02 | 41 |
| ST62E10 | 256 |
| TLC549 | 109 |
| TLC555 | 85 |
| ULN2803 | 52, 140 |

## A

| | |
|---|---|
| A/D converter | 63, 109, 178 |
| ACK | 130, 132 |
| Acknowledge | 162 |
| AND | 39, 60 |
| Auto Feed | 130, 132 |

## B

| | |
|---|---|
| Base address | 35 |
| Baud rate | 49, 247, 257 |
| Break state | 39 |
| Busy | 130, 132 |

## C

| | |
|---|---|
| Capacitance | 85 |
| Centronics | 129, 135 |
| Chip Select | 148 |
| Clock | 99 |
| CloseCOM | 24, 26 |
| COM1 | 21, 29 |
| COM2 | 21, 29 |
| Common-emitter circuit | 76 |
| Crystal | 257 |
| /CS line | 110 |
| CTS | 22, 27 |

## D

| | |
|---|---|
| D/A converter | 137. 178 |
| dB | 229 |
| DCD | 22, 24 |
| DECLARE | 11 |
| Delay | 12, 13 |
| Delayus | 44 |
| Delphi | 16 |
| Dielectric | 85 |
| Digital counter | 205 |
| Digital voltmeter | 69 |
| DLL | 8 |
| DSR | 22, 24 |
| DTR | 22, 25, 41 |
| DWord | 17 |
| Dynamic range | 229 |

## E

| | |
|---|---|
| ECP | 133 |
| Edges | 82 |
| EKG | 95 |
| EPP | 133 |
| EPROM | 153, 256 |
| Error | 130, 132 |
| Excel | 16, 218 |

EXOR . . . . . . . . . . . . . . . . . . . . . . . . . . . . 60
Exponential function . . . . . . . . . . . . 68, 198
external . . . . . . . . . . . . . . . . . . . . . . . . . . 17

**F**

Flip-flop . . . . . . . . . . . . . . . . . . . . . . . . . 199
Frequency . . . . . . . . . . . . . . . . . . . . 81, 137
Function generator . . . . . . . . . . . . . . . 137

**H**

Handshake lines . . . . . . . . . . . . . . . . 23, 57
Humidity . . . . . . . . . . . . . . . . . . . . . . . . . 85
Humidity sensor . . . . . . . . . . . . . . . . . . . 85

**I**

I2C bus . . . . . . . . . . . . . . . . . . . . . . . . . . 161
Init . . . . . . . . . . . . . . . . . . . . . . . . 130, 132
InPort . . . . . . . . . . . . . . . . . . . . . . . . 11, 39
Input resistance . . . . . . . . . . . . . . . . . . . 71
Integer . . . . . . . . . . . . . . . . . . . . . . . . . . . 17

**J**

Joystick . . . . . . . . . . . . . . . . . . . . . . . . . . 189

**L**

LDR . . . . . . . . . . . . . . . . . . . . . . . . . . . . . 65
LED . . . . . . . . . . . . . . . . . . . . . . . . . 23, 202
Limit frequency . . . . . . . . . . . . . . . . . . . 82
Linearisation . . . . . . . . . . . . . . . 67, 86, 198
Logic analyser . . . . . . . . . . . . . . . 120, 174
LPT1 . . . . . . . . . . . . . . . . . . . . . . . . 129, 132
LPT2 . . . . . . . . . . . . . . . . . . . . . . . . 129, 132

**M**

Macro . . . . . . . . . . . . . . . . . . . . . . . . . . . . 15
Macro compiler . . . . . . . . . . . . . . . . . . . 269
Mark . . . . . . . . . . . . . . . . . . . . . . . . . . . . 267
Microcontroller . . . . . . . 145, 251, 256, 267

Mixer . . . . . . . . . . . . . . . . . . . . . . . . . . . 213
Multi Processor mode . . . . . . . . . . . . . . 267

**N**

9-bit mode . . . . . . . . . . . . . . . . . . . . . . . 267
NAND . . . . . . . . . . . . . . . . . . . . . . . 60, 122
NOR . . . . . . . . . . . . . . . . . . . . . . . . . . . . . 60
NPN transistor . . . . . . . . . . . . . . . . . . . . 76
NTC . . . . . . . . . . . . . . . . . . . . . . . . 65, 194

**O**

Offset . . . . . . . . . . . . . . . . . . . . . . . . . . . . 36
Ohmmeter . . . . . . . . . . . . . . . . . . . . . . . 210
OpenCOM . . . . . . . . . . . . . 23–26, 132, 276
Operational amplilfier . . . . . . . . . . . . . . 66
Optocoupler . . . . . . . . . . . . . . . . . . . . . . 41
OR . . . . . . . . . . . . . . . . . . . . . . . . . . . . . . 60
Oscillator . . . . . . . . . . . . . . . . . . . . . . . . 85
OutPort . . . . . . . . . . . . . . . . . . . . . . . 11, 36

**P**

Paintbox . . . . . . . . . . . . . . . . . . . . . . . . . 220
PC loudspeaker . . . . . . . . . . . . . . . . . . . 10
PCHAR . . . . . . . . . . . . . . . . . . . . . . . . . . 29
PCM format . . . . . . . . . . . . . . . . . . . . . 213
PE . . . . . . . . . . . . . . . . . . . . . . . . 130, 132
PIO . . . . . . . . . . . . . . . . . . . . . . . . . . . . . 10
Port chip . . . . . . . . . . . . . . . . . . . . . . . . 145
Power driver . . . . . . . . . . . . . . . . . . . . . . 52
Printer cable . . . . . . . . . . . . . . . . . . . . . 129
PS/2-compatible . . . . . . . . . . . . . . . . . . 134

**Q**

Quiescent state . . . . . . . . . . . . . . . . . . . 162

**R**

RC network . . . . . . . . . . . . . . . . . . . . 63, 66
ReadByte . . . . . . . . . . . . . . . . . . . . . . . . . 24
Real . . . . . . . . . . . . . . . . . . . . . . . . . . . . . 17

# Appendix

RealTime . . . . . . . . . . . . . . . . . . . . . . . . . 34
Real-time capability . . . . . . . . . . . . . . 13, 46
Register address . . . . . . . . . . . . . . . . . . . 35
Resolution . . . . . . . . . . . . . . . . . . . . . . . . 63
RGB . . . . . . . . . . . . . . . . . . . . . . . . . . . . 233
RS232 . . . . . . . . . . . . . . . . . . . 23, 99, 247
RTS . . . . . . . . . . . . . . . . . . . . . . . . . . 22, 41
RxD . . . . . . . . . . . . . . . . . . . . . . . . . 22, 247

**S**

Schmitt trigger . . . . . . . . . . . . . . . . . . . . 63
SCL . . . . . . . . . . . . . . . . . . . . . . . . . . . . 161
ScrollBar . . . . . . . . . . . . . . . . . . . . . . . . . 31
SDA . . . . . . . . . . . . . . . . . . . . . . . . . . . . 161
Select . . . . . . . . . . . . . . . . . . . . . 130, 132
Semiconductor relay . . . . . . . . . . . . . . . 41
SendByte . . . . . . . . . . . . . . . . . . . . . . . . 24
Serial interface . . . . . . . . . . . . . . . . . . . 21
Servo . . . . . . . . . . . . . . . . . . . . . . . . . . . 44
Shift register . . . . . . . . . . . . . . . . . . . . . 99
Sine-wave generator . . . . . . . . . . . . . . 138
Single-chip solution . . . . . . . . . . . . . . . 252
SLCT IN . . . . . . . . . . . . . . . . . . . . 130, 132
Slider . . . . . . . . . . . . . . . . . . . . . . . . . . . 31
Sound card . . . . . . . . . . . . . . . . . . . . . . 213
Space . . . . . . . . . . . . . . . . . . . . . . . . . . 267
Square-wave signal . . . . . . . . . . . . . . . . 31
Start condition . . . . . . . . . . . . . . . . . . . 162
stdcall . . . . . . . . . . . . . . . . . . . . . . . . . . 17
Stepping motor . . . . . . . . . . . . . . . 52, 140
Stop condition . . . . . . . . . . . . . . . . . . . 162
Stopwatch . . . . . . . . . . . . . . . . . . . . . . 120
Storage oscilloscope . . . . . . . . . . . . . . 180
Strobe . . . . . . . . . . . . . . . . . 100, 130, 132

**T**

Temperature . . . . . . . . . . . . . . . . . . . . . . 85
Temperature coefficient . . . . . . . . . . . . 86
Tiime base . . . . . . . . . . . . . . . . . . . . . . . 81
Timeout . . . . . . . . . . . . . . . . . . . . . . . . . 64
Timer . . . . . . . . . . . . . . . . . . 31, 47, 85, 199
Tone burst . . . . . . . . . . . . . . . . . . . . . . 229

Tone generator . . . . . . . . . . . . . . . . . . . 229
Triac . . . . . . . . . . . . . . . . . . . . . . . . . . . 41
TTL . . . . . . . . . . . . . . . . . . . . . . . . 132, 194
TTL level . . . . . . . . . . . . . . . . . . . . . . . . 23
TxD . . . . . . . . . . . . . . . . . . 22, 39, 41, 247
TXD . . . . . . . . . . . . . . . . . . . . . . . . . . . . 24

**U**

UART . . . . . . . . . . . . . . . . . . . . 34, 49, 267
Unit . . . . . . . . . . . . . . . . . . . . . . . . . . . . 30
USES . . . . . . . . . . . . . . . . . . . . . . . . . . . 30

**V**

V/f converter . . . . . . . . . . . . . . . . . . . . . 90
VBA . . . . . . . . . . . . . . . . . . . . . . . . 16, 216
Video capture card . . . . . . . . . . . . . . . . 233
Visual Basic . . . . . . . . . . . . . . . . . . . . . . 11

**W**

Watchdog . . . . . . . . . . . . . . . . . . . . . . . 259
Windows 95 . . . . . . . . . . . . . . . . . . . . . . 9
Windows 98 . . . . . . . . . . . . . . . . . . . . . . 10
Windows NT . . . . . . . . . . . . . . . . . . . 10, 24
Word . . . . . . . . . . . . . . . . . . . . . . . 16, 216

**X**

X–Y plotter . . . . . . . . . . . . . . . . . . . . . . 120

**Z**

Zener diode . . . . . . . . . . . . . . . . . . . 71, 167
Zero crossing . . . . . . . . . . . . . . . . . . . . . 41
ZN426 . . . . . . . . . . . . . . . . . . . . . . . . . 137

# PORT.DLL Reference

All function names must be stated in capital letters. Some functions do not work under Windows NT. The DLL may be located in the System directory, the Windows directory or the Applications directory.

## Port Commands

(Cannot be used under Windows NT.)

INPORT
Parameter: address (0-65535)
Reads a port.
The returned value is the content (byte) of the indicated port address.

Declaration in Delphi:
```
Function INPORT(PortAddr: Word): byte; stdcall; external
   'port.dll';
```

Declaration in VB and VBA:
```
Declare Function INPORT Lib "Port" (ByVal p%) As Integer
```

OUTPORT
Parameter: address (0-65535)
Outputs to a port.
Returned value: none.

Declaration in Delphi:
```
Procedure OUTPORT(PortAddr: Word; Data: byte); stdcall;
   external 'port.dll';
```

Declaration in VB and VBA:
```
Declare Function INPORT Lib "Port" (ByVal p%) As Integer
```

## Serial Interface Routines

OPENCOM
Parameter: character string as a zero-terminated string
Opens the serial interface.
Returned value: '0' in the event of an error.

Declaration in Delphi:
```
Function OPENCOM(S: PCHAR):Integer; stdcall; external
   'port.dll';
```

Declaration in VB and VBA:
```
Declare Sub OPENCOM Lib "Port" (ByVal A$)
Declare Function OPENCOM Lib "Port" (ByVal A$) As Integer
```

Note: the character string is passed directly to Windows. The following call can be used under Windows 95/98/NT:

```
OPENCOM   "COM2: baud=19200 data=8 parity=N stop=1"
```

The following call also works under Windows 95/98:

```
OPENCOM   "COM2,19200,N,8,1"
```

---

CLOSECOM
Parameter: none.
Closes the serial interface.
Returned value: none.

Declaration in Delphi:
```
Procedure CLOSECOM; stdcall; external 'port.dll';
```

Declaration in VB and VBA:
```
Declare Sub CLOSECOM Lib "Port" ()
```

---

READBYTE
Parameter: none.
Reads a byte from the serial interface. This interface must have been previously opened using OpenCom.
Returned value: '-1' in the event of an error, otherwise the received byte

Declaration in Delphi:
```
Function READBYTE: WORD; stdcall; external 'port.dll';
```

Declaration in VB and VBA:
```
Declare Function READBYTE Lib "Port" () As Integer
```

---

SENDBYTE
Parameter: one byte (0-255)
Sends a byte via the serial interface. This interface must have been previously opened using OpenCom.

Declaration in Delphi:
```
Procedure SENDBYTE(Value: WORD); stdcall; external
  'port.dll';
```

Declaration in VB and VBA:
```
Declare Sub SENDBYTE Lib "Port" (ByVal B%)
```

---

DSR
Parameter: none.
Polls the serial port line DSR. This interface must have been previously opened using OpenCom.
Returned value: line state (1/0)

Declaration in Delphi:
```
Function DSR: WORD; stdcall; external 'port.dll';
```

Declaration in VB and VBA:
```
Declare Function DSR Lib "Port" () As Integer
```

CTS
Parameter: none.
Polls the serial port line CTS. This interface must have been previously opened using OpenCom.
Returned value: line state (1/0)

Declaration in Delphi:
```
Function CTS: WORD; stdcall; external 'port.dll';
```

Declaration in VB and VBA:
```
Declare Function CTS Lib "Port" () As Integer
```

RI
Parameter: none.
Polls the serial port line RI. This interface must have been previously opened using OpenCom.
Returned value: line state (1/0)

Declaration in Delphi:
```
Function RI: WORD; stdcall; external 'port.dll';
```

Declaration in VB and VBA:
```
Declare Function RI Lib "Port" () As Integer
```

DCD
Parameter: none.
Polls the serial port line DCD. This interface must have been previously opened using OpenCom.
Returned value: line state (1/0)

Declaration in Delphi:
```
Function DCD: WORD; stdcall; external 'port.dll';
```

Declaration in VB and VBA:
```
Declare Function DCD Lib "Port" () As Integer
```

RTS
Parameter: value (1/0)
Sets the serial port line RTS. This interface must have been previously opened using OpenCom.

Declaration in Delphi:
```
Procedure RTS(Value: WORD); stdcall; external 'port.dll';
```

Declaration in VB and VBA:
```
Declare Sub RI Lib "Port" (ByVal Value%)
```

TXD
Parameter: value (1/0)
Sets the serial port line TxD. This interface must have been previously opened using OpenCom.

Declaration in Delphi:
```
Procedure TXD(Value: WORD); stdcall; external 'port.dll';
```

Declaration in VB and VBA:

```
Declare Sub TXD Lib "Port" (ByVal Value%)
```

DTR
Parameter: value (1/0)
Sets the serial port line DTR. This interface must have been previously opened using OpenCom.

Declaration in Delphi:

```
Procedure DTR(Value: WORD); stdcall; external 'port.dll';
```

Declaration in VB and VBA:

```
Declare Sub DTR Lib "Port" (ByVal Value%)
```

TIMEOUT
Parameter: time interval in milliseconds
Sets the timeout for the serial interface. This interface must have been previously opened using OpenCom.
If no character is received within this interval, READBYTE is terminated and '-1' is returned.

Declaration in Delphi:

```
Procedure TIMEOUT(Value: WORD); stdcall; external
   'port.dll';
```

Declaration in VB and VBA:

```
Declare Sub TIMEOUT Lib "Port" (ByVal Value%)
```

## Sound Card Routines

SOUNDIS
Parameter: none.
Determines whether a sound card is present.
Returned value: '0' or '-1', or 'True' or 'False'

Declaration in Delphi:

```
Function SOUNDIS: Boolean; stdcall; external 'port.dll';
```

Declaration in VB and VBA:

```
Declare Function SOUNDIS Lib "Port" () As Integer
```

SOUNDCAPIN
Parameter: none.
The sound card input properties are output in a MessageBox.
Returned value: none.

Declaration in Delphi:

```
Procedure SOUNDCAPIN; stdcall; external 'port.dll';
```

Declaration in VB and VBA:

```
Declare Sub SOUNDCAPIN Lib "Port" ()
```

SOUNDCAPOUT
Parameter: none.
The sound card output properties are output in a MessageBox.
Returned value: none.

Declaration in Delphi:
```
Procedure SOUNDCAPOUT; stdcall; external 'port.dll';
```

Declaration in VB and VBA:
```
Declare Sub SOUNDCAPOUT Lib "Port" ()
```

SOUNDIN
Parameters: storage location and memory size (in bytes)
Starts sound recording and stores the data in the buffer memory specified by the parameters.
Returned value: none.

Declaration in Delphi:
```
Procedure SOUNDIN(Buffer: Pchar; Size: DWORD); stdcall;
   external 'port.dll';
```

Declaration in VB and VBA:
```
Declare Sub SOUNDIN Lib "Port" (ByVal A$, ByVal Gr As
   Long)
```

SOUNDOUT
Parameters: storage location and memory size (in bytes)
Starts sound playback of the data in the buffer memory specified by the parameters
Returned value: none.

Declaration in Delphi:
```
Procedure SOUNDOUT(Buffer: Pchar; Size: DWORD); stdcall;
   external 'port.dll';
```

Declaration in VB and VBA:
```
Declare Sub SOUNDOUT Lib "Port" (ByVal A$, ByVal Gr As
   Long)
```

SOUNDGETRATE
Parameter: none.
Queries the sample rate setting.
Returned value: sample rate in samples/s (for example, 11025).

Declaration in Delphi:
```
Function SOUNDGETRATE: WORD; stdcall; external
   'port.dll';
```

Declaration in VB and VBA:
```
Declare Function SOUNDGETRATE Lib "Port" () As Integer
```

SOUNDSETRATE
Parameter: sample rate in samples/s
Sets the sample rate.
Returned value: previous sample rate in samples/s. (for example, 11025).

Declaration in Delphi:

```
Function SOUNDSETRATE(Rate: DWORD): DWORD; stdcall;
  external 'port.dll';
```

Declaration in VB and VBA:

```
Declare Function SOUNDSETRATE Lib "Port" (ByVal Rate As
  Long) As Long
```

SOUNGETBYTES
Parameter: none.
Queries the number of bytes per sample.
Returned value: '1' or '2'. One byte corresponds to 8 bits/sample; two bytes corresponds to 16 bits/sample.

Declaration in Delphi:

```
Function SOUNDGETBYTES: WORD; stdcall; external
  'port.dll';
```

Declaration in VB and VBA:

```
Declare Function SOUNDSETRATE Lib "Port" () As Integer
```

SOUNDSETBYTES
Parameter: 1/2
Sets the number of bytes per sample.
Returned value: '1' or '2'. One byte corresponds to 8 bits/sample; two bytes corresponds to 16 bits/sample.

Declaration in Delphi:

```
Function SOUNDGETBYTES: WORD; stdcall; external
  'port.dll';
```

Declaration in VB and VBA:

```
Declare Function SOUNDSETRATE Lib "Port" () As Integer
```

## Joystick Routines

JOYX
Parameter: none.
Requests the X position.
Returned value: position a numerical value.

Declaration in Delphi:

```
Function JOYX: DWORD; stdcall; external 'port.dll';
```

Declaration in VB and VBA:

```
Declare Function JOYX Lib "Port" () As Long
```

JOYY
Parameter: none.
Requests the Y position.
Returned value: position as a numerical value.

Declaration in Delphi:
```
Function JOYY: DWORD; stdcall; external 'port.dll';
```

Declaration in VB and VBA:
```
Declare Function JOYY Lib "Port" () As Long
```

JOYZ
Parameter: none.
Requests the Z position.
Returned value: position as a numerical value.

Declaration in Delphi:
```
Function JOYZ: DWORD; stdcall; external 'port.dll';
```

Declaration in VB and VBA:
```
Declare Function JOYZ Lib "Port" () As Long
```

JOYR
Parameter: none.
Requests the R position.
Returned value: position as a numerical value.

Declaration in Delphi:
```
Function JOYR: DWORD; stdcall; external 'port.dll';
```

Declaration in VB and VBA:
```
Declare Function JOYR Lib "Port" () As Long
```

JOYU
Parameter: none.
Requests the U position.
Returned value: position as a numerical value.

Declaration in Delphi:
```
Function JOYU: DWORD; stdcall; external 'port.dll';
```

Declaration in VB and VBA:
```
Declare Function JOYU Lib "Port" () As Long
```

JOYV
Parameter: none.
Requests the V position.
Returned value: position as a numerical value.

Declaration in Delphi:
```
Function JOYV: DWORD; stdcall; external 'port.dll';
```

Declaration in VB and VBA:
```
Declare Function JOYV Lib "Port" () As Long
```

JOYBUTTON
Parameter: none.
Button polling.
Returned value: button as a numerical value.

Declaration in Delphi:
```
Function JOYBUTTON: DWORD; stdcall; external 'port.dll';
```

Declaration in VB and VBA:
```
Declare Function JOYBUTTON Lib "Port" () As Long
```

JOYSTICK
Parameter: seven variables for receiving the values
Complete polling in a single call.
Returned value: none.

Declaration in Delphi:
```
Procedure JOYSTICK(VAR X,Y,Z,R,U,V,B: DWORD); stdcall;
    external 'port.dll';
```

Declaration in VB and VBA:
```
Declare Sub JOYSTICK Lib "Port" (ByVal X As Long, ByVal Y
    As Long ...)
```

## Timing Routines

DELAY
Parameter: time in milliseconds
Delay in the milliseconds range.
Returned value: none.

Declaration in Delphi:
```
Procedure DELAY(ms: WORD); stdcall; external 'port.dll';
```

Declaration in VB and VBA:
```
Declare Sub DELAY Lib "Port" (ByVal ms%)
```

TIMEINIT
Parameter: none.
Sets the milliseconds timing counter to zero.
Returned value: none.

Declaration in Delphi:
```
Procedure TIMEINIT; stdcall; external 'port.dll';
```

Declaration in VB and VBA:
```
Declare Sub TIMEINIT Lib "Port" ()
```

TIMEREAD
Parameter: none.
Reads the milliseconds timer. The result the number of milliseconds that have elapsed since TIMEINT was last called.
Returned value: milliseconds as a numerical value

Declaration in Delphi:
```
Function TIMEREAD: DWORD; stdcall; external 'port.dll';
```

Declaration in VB and VBA:
```
Declare Function TIMEREAD Lib "Port" () As Long
```

TIMEINITUS
Parameter: none.
Sets the microseconds timing counter to zero.
Returned value: none.

Declaration in Delphi:
```
Procedure TIMEINITUS; stdcall; external 'port.dll';
```

Declaration in VB and VBA:
```
Declare Sub TIMEINITUS Lib "Port" ()
```

TIMEREADUS
Parameter: none.
Reads the microseconds timer. The result the number of microseconds that have elapsed since TIMEINTUS was last called.
Returned value: microseconds as a numerical value

Declaration in Delphi:
```
Function TIMEREADUS: DWORD; stdcall; external 'port.dll';
```

Declaration in VB and VBA:
```
Declare Function TIMEREADUS Lib "Port" () As Long
```

REALTIME
Parameter: '0' or '1'.
Sets the highest priority. This call is useful with time-critical outputs.
It should be activated only briefly, since it causes other programs to run more slowly.
Returned value: none.

Declaration in Delphi:
```
Procedure REALTIME(d: WORD); stdcall; external
    'port.dll';
```

Declaration in VB and VBA:
```
Declare Sub TIMEREADUS Lib "Port" (ByVal d%)
```

## CD-ROM Contents

The CD-ROM contains a directory for each chapter of the book. Each chapter directory contains all respective sample programs in Visual Basic 5, Delphi 3 or Delphi 4, in both source code and in compiled form. The required PORT.DLL is located together with the compiled programs in each subdirectory . This DLL must be copied to the Windows directory when working with your own programs.

The 'Reference' directory contains the complete documentation for PORT.DLL in text format for Winword 6, WRI format and TXT format.

The 'Setup' directory contains the program SETUP.EXE, which must be run if Visual Basic does not work correctly. This will install an auxiliary file in the directory 'PC-interfaces'. On de-installation this file will be automatically deleted.

In addition to the program listings contained in the book, the CD-ROM includes two complete application programs:

- **COMPUNI.EXE:** Compact Universal, the application program for the universal interface, is located in the Chapter 8 / Delphi 4 directory.

- **SSCANP.EXE:** SoundScan, a complete oscilloscope for the Soundcard, is located in the Chapter 14 / Delphi 3 directory.

System requirements for using the CD-ROM:

- **PC:** 486, Pentium or better

- **Operating system:** Windows 95/98 or Windows NT.

- **Recommended:** Visual Basic 5 and Delphi 4.